First Star
The Blue-Pillowed Sky
A Shiny Golden Path
Rainbow Bridge
Slide Down the Sky
From Sea to Shining Sea
Time for Dreams
Across the World
Over the Moon
Sound of the Sea
Promises to Keep

I saw a star slide down the sky,
Blinding the north as it went by,
Too burning and too quick to hold,
Too lovely to be bought or sold,
Good only to make wishes on
And then forever to be gone.

—Sara Teasdale

Slide Down the Sky

An anthology
compiled and edited by

Zena Sutherland and **Marilyn F. Cunningham**

Program Authors

Carl Bereiter
Marlene Scardamalia
Ann Brown
Valerie Anderson
Joseph Campione
Walter Kintsch

Open Court
La Salle, Illinois

President and Publisher
M. Blouke Carus

Education Director
Carl Bereiter

Project Coordination
Marsha Roit

Project Planning and Implementation
Thomas G. Anderson,
Commonwealth Strategies, Inc.

Senior Editor
Marilyn Cunningham

Permissions
Diane Sikora

Art Direction
Todd Sanders

Cover Design
James Buddenbaum

Acknowledgments

Grateful acknowledgment is given to the following publishers and copyright owners for permission granted to reprint selections from their publications. All possible care has been taken to trace ownership and secure permission for each selection included.

Atheneum Publishers, for "Wind Song," from *I Feel the Same Way* by Lilian Moore; copyright © 1967 Lilian Moore.

Betty Baker, for an excerpt from *Partners* by Betty Baker; text copyright © 1978 by Betty Baker.

Eve Bunting, for "Where's Willie?" by Eve Bunting; copyright © 1986 by Eve Bunting. "Where's Willie?" was first published, in slightly different form, in *Cricket* Magazine.

Marchette Chute, for "Tracks in the Snow," from *Around and About* by Marchette Chute; copyright 1957 (Dutton), renewed 1985.

Crown Publishers, Inc., for excerpts from *Animal Fact/Animal Fable* by Seymour Simon; text copyright © 1979 by Seymour Simon.

Delacorte Press/Seymour Lawrence and William Jay Smith, for "Moon," excerpted from the book *Laughing Time: Nonsense Poems* by William Jay Smith; copyright © 1953, 1955, 1956, 1957, 1959, 1968, 1974, 1977, 1980 by William Jay Smith.

Doubleday & Company, Inc., for *Emma* by Wendy Kesselman, illustrated by Barbara Cooney; text copyright © 1980 by Wendy Kesselman, illustrations copyright © 1980 by Barbara Cooney Porter.

E. P. Dutton, a division of New American Library, and McIntosh and Otis, Inc., for an adaptation of *The Balancing Girl* by Berniece Rabe; text copyright © 1981 by Berniece Rabe.

Farrar, Straus and Giroux, Inc., for an adaptation of "The Parakeet Named Dreidel," from *The Power of Light* by I. B. Singer; copyright © 1975, 1976 by Isaac Bashevis Singer. This version originally appeared in *Cricket* Magazine.

Greenwillow Books, a division of William Morrow & Company, for "Alex's Bone," from *More Alex and the Cat* by Helen V. Griffith, pictures by Donald Carrick; text copyright © 1983 by Helen V. Griffith, illustrations copyright © 1983 by Donald Carrick.

Harcourt Brace Jovanovich, Inc., for "Fog," from *Chicago Poems* by Carl Sandburg; copyright 1916 by Holt, Rinehart and Winston, renewed 1944 by Carl Sandburg.

Harper & Row, Publishers, Inc.: for complete text (abridged and adapted) of *Brothers: A Hebrew Legend* by Florence Bernstein Freedman, copyright © 1985 by Florence Bernstein Freedman; and for "Tommy" and "Cynthia in the Snow," from *Bronzeville Boys and Girls* by Gwendolyn Brooks, copyright © 1956 by Gwendolyn Brooks Blakely.

Illustrators

Franz Altschuler (50–51, 161), Victor Ambrus (33–35), Bill and Judie Anderson (81, 111, 113–114), Enrico Arno (134–135, 142), James Arnosky (9–11, 96), L. Leslie Brooke (2–5), Donald Carrick (139–141, 156–159), Tony Chen (62), Gwen Connelly (70, 73), Barbara Cooney (84–85, 87–88), Jim Cummins (145, 148, 150), David Cunningham (45–49, 138), Lydia Dabcovich (153, 155), Tomie de Paola (19–24), Bert Dodson (172–173, 175, 177), Tom Dunnington (116–117), Pat Dypold (cover), Mike Eagle (8), Larry Frederick (185, 187, 189), Don Freeman (13–14, 16–17), Imero Gobatto (43, 69), Marylin Hafner (25–31), Michael Hague (6–7, 109), Friso Henstra (63–67), Trina Schart Hyman (133, 162–167, 180–181, 183–184), Ann Iosa (190, 192–193, 195–196), Arnold Lobel (57–58, 60), Guilio Maestro (32, 128, 130), Dick Martin (12), Robert Masheris (44), Les Morrill (169–171), Lynn Munsinger (89, 91, 93, 95), Tak Murakami (76–79), Phill Renaud (100–101), Symeon Shimin (103–104, 106–108), Dan Siculan (2–5, 36–40, 97, 118–123), Phero Thomas (61), Justin Wager (32), Jack Wallen (136–137), John Walter, Jr. (124–127), Jan Wills (53–56)

Photography

Field Museum of Natural History (80), John E. Hall (99), Ellis Herwig, The Marilyn Gartman Agency (48), Everett C. Johnson, The Marilyn Gartman Agency (48), National Broadcasting Company (82), Photo Reserve Inc. (83), Photri, The Marilyn Gartman Agency (48)

Contents

Unit One
Getting Acquainted

Unit Two
Nature

Unit Three
Work and Play

Unit Four
Think Again

Unit Five
Surprises

Unit One
Getting Acquainted

Johnny Crow's Garden

L. LESLIE BROOKE

Johnny Crow
Would dig and sow
Till he made a little garden.

And the lion
Had a green and yellow
tie on
In Johnny Crow's garden.

And the pig
Danced a jig
In Johnny Crow's garden.

And the whale
Told a very long tale
In Johnny Crow's garden.

3

And the rat
Wore a feather in his hat.

But the bear
Had nothing to wear
In Johnny Crow's garden.

So the ape
Took his measure with
a tape
In Johnny Crow's garden.

And the fox
Put them all in the stocks
In Johnny Crow's garden.

But Johnny Crow
He let them go.

And they all sat down to
    their dinner in a row
In Johnny Crow's garden.

5

The Fox and the Crow

AESOP

One time a sly fox saw a crow fly from a kitchen window to the branch of a tree. The crow was holding a big piece of cheese in his beak.

"How I would like to have that piece of cheese," said the fox to herself. She thought and thought about how she could get the cheese.

After a while the fox went over to the foot of the tree and said, "Good morning, Master Crow. My, you are looking fine today! Surely you are the most beautiful of all birds. What's more, no bird in the world can sing more sweetly than you. How I would love to hear you sing!"

The crow was very pleased to hear all these nice things said about him.

"I will be glad to sing you a little song," he said. He stretched out his neck, opened his beak wide, and sang at the top of his lungs, "Caw, caw, caw!"

At once the big piece of cheese fell to the ground, and the hungry fox gobbled it up.

"Thank you, Master Crow," said the fox. "My, but that was a fine piece of cheese!" Then off she trotted.

"Oh, what have I done!" said the crow to himself. "Never again will I trust a flatterer!"

The Milkmaid and Her Pail

AESOP

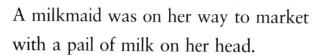

A milkmaid was on her way to market with a pail of milk on her head.

As she was walking along, she said to herself, "With the money I get from this milk, I am going to buy some setting eggs. From the eggs I will get some chicks. Then I will raise the chicks until they are big enough to sell. With the money I get from the chickens, I will buy a beautiful gown. When I wear the gown, I will look so beautiful that everyone will admire me. But I shall act very proudly. I will shrug my shoulders like this."

As she shrugged her shoulders, she tossed her head back. The pail of milk tumbled down, and the milk spilled all over the ground.

"Oh dear!" exclaimed the milkmaid. "Now there will be no gown, and no one will admire me. I won't have any chickens or any eggs, and now I don't even have the milk. But I have learned one thing—don't count your chickens before they are hatched."

8

The Little Pot

JACOB and WILHELM GRIMM

Once upon a time a little girl lived all alone with her mother. They were so poor that often they did not have enough to eat.

One morning the little girl sat down to eat her breakfast of sweet pudding. "Mother," said the girl, "where is your bowl of pudding?"

Her mother burst into tears. "My poor child, there isn't any more pudding. There isn't a scrap of food left in the house."

"Here, take half of my pudding," said the good little girl. "And don't worry. I'll find some food for us."

So after breakfast the girl set off to gather roots and berries. As she followed the path deep into the forest, she came upon a little house. A woman was sitting on the front steps, singing softly to herself. She looked at the little girl and saw how pale and thin she was. Then the woman disappeared into the house. When she came out again, she was carrying a little pot.

The woman called the girl over and handed her the pot. "My child, this is a magic pot," said the woman. "Just say to the pot, 'Little pot, boil!' It will cook the best sweet pudding you have ever tasted. After you have had enough to eat, say, 'Little pot, stop!' The pot will stop cooking right away."

The little girl thanked the woman. Then she ran home and showed her mother the magic pot. It worked exactly as the woman had said it would. Now the little girl and her mother had more than enough to eat. Day after day they ate all the sweet pudding they wanted.

One day the little girl went to the forest to gather wild flowers. While she was gone, her mother decided to have some sweet pudding. She said the magic words, "Little pot, boil!" The pot cooked pudding until the mother could not eat another bite. But she did not know how to stop the pot from cooking, so it cooked on and on, and on and on.

The pudding bubbled over the top of the pot and onto the kitchen floor. It ran into the other rooms of the house, out into the street, and into the house next door.

Soon the whole street was filled with sweet pudding, and it ran into one house after another. People were running in all directions, trying to escape from the pudding. It seemed as though the little pot wanted to make pudding for the whole world. The pot was making a terrible mess, but nobody knew how to stop it.

Finally, when almost all of the houses were filled with pudding, the little girl came back from the forest. She said, "Little pot, stop!" The little pot stopped cooking right away. The people had to eat their way back home, but nobody minded, for the sweet pudding was the best anyone had ever tasted.

The Goops

GELETT BURGESS

The Goops they lick their fingers,
And the Goops they lick their knives;
They spill their broth on the tablecloth—
Oh, they lead disgusting lives!
The Goops they talk while eating,
And loud and fast they chew;
And that is why I'm glad that I
Am not a Goop—are you?

Corduroy

DON FREEMAN

[PART 1]

Corduroy is a bear who once lived in the toy department of a big store. Day after day he waited with all the other animals and dolls for somebody to come along and take him home.

The store was always filled with shoppers buying all sorts of things, but no one ever seemed to want a small bear in green overalls.

Then one morning a little girl stopped and looked straight into Corduroy's bright eyes. "Oh, Mommy!" she said. "Look! There's the very bear I've always wanted."

"Not today, dear." Her mother sighed. "I've spent too much already. Besides, he doesn't look new. He's lost the button to one of his shoulder straps."

Corduroy watched them sadly as they walked away. "I didn't know I'd lost a button," he said to himself. "Tonight I'll go and see if I can find it."

Late that evening, when all the shoppers had gone and the doors were shut and locked, Corduroy climbed carefully down from his shelf and began searching everywhere on the floor for his lost button.

Suddenly he felt the floor moving under him! Quite by accident he had stepped onto an escalator—and up he went! "Could this be a mountain?" he wondered. "I think I've always wanted to climb a mountain."

He stepped off the escalator as it reached the next floor, and there, before his eyes, was a most amazing sight—tables and chairs and lamps and sofas, and rows and rows of beds. "This must be a palace!" Corduroy gasped. "I guess I've always wanted to live in a palace."

He wandered around admiring the furniture. "This must be a bed," he said. "I've always wanted to sleep in a bed." And up he crawled onto a large, thick mattress.

All at once he saw something small and round. "Why, here's my button!" he cried. And he tried to pick it up. But, like all the other buttons on the mattress, it was tied down tight.

He yanked and pulled with both paws until POP! Off came the button—and off the mattress Corduroy toppled, *bang* into a tall floor lamp. Over it fell with a crash!

[PART 2]

Corduroy didn't know it, but there was someone else awake in the store. The night watchman was going his rounds on the floor above. When he heard the crash, he came dashing down the escalator.

"Now who in the world did that!" he exclaimed. "Somebody must be hiding around here!"

He flashed his light under and over sofas and beds until he came to the biggest bed of all. And there he saw two fuzzy brown ears sticking up from under the cover.

"Hello!" he said. "How did *you* get upstairs?"

The watchman tucked Corduroy under his arm and carried him down the escalator and set him on the shelf in the toy department with the other animals and dolls.

Corduroy was just waking up when the first customers came into the store in the morning. And there, looking at him with a wide, warm smile, was the same little girl he'd seen only the day before.

"I'm Lisa," she said, "and you're going to be my very own bear. Last night I counted what I've saved in my piggy bank, and my mother said I could bring you home."

"Shall I put him in a box for you?" the saleslady asked.

"Oh, no thank you," Lisa answered. And she carried Corduroy home in her arms.

She ran all the way up four flights of stairs, into her family's apartment, and straight to her own room.

Corduroy blinked. There was a chair and a chest of drawers, and alongside a girl-size bed stood a little bed just the right size for him. The room was small, nothing like that enormous palace in the department store.

"This must be home," he said. "I *know* I've always wanted a home!"

Lisa sat down with Corduroy on her lap and began to sew a button on his overalls. "I like you the way you are," she said, "but you'll be more comfortable with your shoulder strap fastened."

"You must be a friend," said Corduroy. "I've always wanted a friend."

"Me too!" said Lisa, and she gave him a big hug.

 # Bill and Pete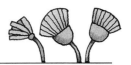

TOMIE DE PAOLA

William Everett Crocodile lived on the banks of the River Nile with his mama.

One day, Mama said, "William Everett, now that you have nice crocodile teeth, we must go to Mr. Hippo's store and get you a toothbrush before you start school tomorrow."

William Everett liked Mr. Hippo's store because it was full of things. He and Mama walked up one aisle and down another.

They stopped in front of the toothbrush counter. "You may choose your own toothbrush, William Everett," Mama said.

William Everett looked and looked.

"Hi!" said a toothbrush. "What's your name?"

"My name's William Everett. What's yours?"

"Pete," said the toothbrush.

"I found the toothbrush I want, Mama," said William Everett. "His name is Pete."

"Good," said Mama. "We can go home now."

So Pete became William Everett's toothbrush. And his best friend, too.

The next morning Mama said, "William Everett, wake up. It's time to go to school."

"Oh, Mama," William Everett said. "I can't wait to read and write and learn all about crocodile history."

"Someday I will be proud of you, William Everett," Mama said.

"Now, class," said Ms. Ibis. "Today we are going to learn the alphabet. Then we will be able to write our names. Now, repeat after me. . . ."

The little crocodiles repeated after Ms. Ibis. "A—B—C—D—E—F—G . . ." They said the whole alphabet. They said the letters over and over again until they knew all of them by heart.

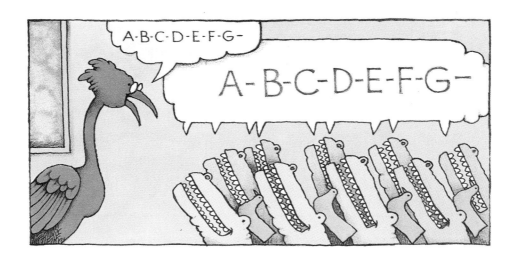

"Well, William Everett," said Mama. "What did you learn in school today?"

"William Everett, say the alphabet," said Pete. William Everett said every letter without a mistake.

"Oh, William Everett," Mama said. "That was beautiful."

The next day, Ms. Ibis taught the class how to write all the letters.

The little crocodiles wrote the letters over and over until they could write them by heart.

"And what did you learn today, William Everett?" Mama asked.

"William Everett, write the letters," said Pete. William Everett wrote every letter without one mistake.

"You're so smart, William Everett," Mama said. "Someday you will be famous."

"Today, class, we are going to write our names," said Ms. Ibis.

She showed all the little crocodiles just what letters each one had in his or her name. They wrote and wrote and wrote and smiled and smiled and smiled.

The letters spelled out Sam—Jane—John—Kay— Kate—Tom—Amy . . .

They all wrote and smiled some more.

All except William Everett. He had so many letters in his name that he kept forgetting at least one of them.

Poor William Everett. Big tears ran down his nose.

"Is something wrong, William Everett?" Pete asked.

"I'll never learn how to write my name," he cried. "It has too many letters."

"Now, now, William Everett," said Pete. "I think I can help you to write your name and not forget any letters."

He took a pencil and wrote.

"Did you learn something today, William Everett?" asked Mama.

"Yes, Mama, I learned to write my name," said William Everett.

"Oh, Bill." Mama beamed.

That Dog!

NANETTE NEWMAN

[PART 1]

"That dog's barking again," said Mrs. Higgs crossly, looking over the fence that separated the two gardens.

"He's not," said Ben. "He's talking."

"Sounds like barking to me," said Mrs. Higgs.

"It would," said Ben. "Come on, Barnum," he called. "Come and help me with my homework."

"Ridiculous," snorted Mrs. Higgs.

Ben and Barnum had been together for as long as Ben could remember. They had grown up together, and Ben had taught Barnum everything he knew.

"He can't do anything," said Mrs. Higgs.

"He can do tricks," said Ben.

"What sort of tricks?" said Mrs. Higgs.

"Kill!" said Ben, and Barnum stood and put his paws on Mrs. Higgs's shoulders.

"Get him off!" screamed Mrs. Higgs. "You call that a trick?" she said, running up the path.

"Definitely," said Ben.

Sometimes Ben and Barnum played soccer. Other times they spent quiet evenings together, reading. Ben would read aloud to Barnum, and Barnum would put his head in Ben's lap and quietly concentrate on the story. His favorite was *Treasure Island*. He liked the sea songs best.

"That dog's whining," shouted Ben's mother from downstairs.

"He's singing," said Ben.

At night Ben and Barnum slept in the same room. When Ben's mother came in to say good night, Barnum would be lying under his blanket in the corner, yawning and stretching. The minute the door was closed he was on the bed, snuggled up to Ben. In the morning he woke Ben by pushing his cold nose under Ben's chin and licking his ear. Ben was never once late for school.

Barnum cried when Ben was scolded, listened when Ben had a problem, was always ready for some fun, and loved Ben as much as Ben loved him.

[PART 2]

Then, one day, Barnum died.

"He was getting old," said Ben's mother kindly.

"He wasn't," said Ben, crying.

"He had a great life," said Ben's father.

"He didn't suffer," said the veterinarian. "He'd just had

a long and happy life—it was time for him to go. It happens to us all."

"But I didn't want it to happen to Barnum," said Ben.

"I know," said the vet.

Ben gave Barnum a grave with a stone marker, said a prayer, and read Barnum's favorite chapter from *Treasure Island*. Mrs. Higgs looked over the garden fence.

"Here!" she called to Ben. She gave Ben the best rose out of her garden to put on Barnum's grave. She didn't have her cross look on either.

"Thank you," said Ben.

Ben felt as if his heart had broken. He would cry at night when he put out his hand on the bed, forgetting Barnum wasn't there. He was late for school some mornings, and he didn't feel like playing soccer.

Ben's father asked, "Ben, how about our getting another dog?"

"Never!" said Ben. "I never want another dog, not ever."

One day when Ben was coming back from school he heard a whimper. He turned around, and there was a tiny puppy. Ben walked on, and so did the puppy. Ben stopped, and the puppy came and sat on his foot. Ben looked at him.

"I'm lost," the puppy seemed to say.

Ben looked up and down the street. There was no one around. He picked up the puppy. There was no collar on him, and he seemed far too young to be out on his own.

"What am I to do with you?" Ben said.

The puppy had fallen asleep in his arms.

Ben took the puppy home. He fed him, and his father said, "Well, now, let me think. He looks like a stray to me, but we'd better make some inquiries. Would you mind taking care of him until we find him a home?"

"Well, I guess not," said Ben.

The puppy seemed to like Ben's room. He ate a slipper and tore up a book. He made a puddle on the floor, but when Ben explained to him that those habits were meant for the garden, he seemed to understand.

A few days later Ben's father said, "Well, no one's claimed him. I suppose we'll have to take him to the dog pound."

"Tomorrow," said Ben.

That night, Ben sat in his room trying to do his French homework. The puppy woke up and got off his foot. He looked at Ben, trying to get him to play.

"I could never love another dog the way I loved Barnum," said Ben.

The puppy cocked his head to one side and seemed to listen.

"No dog could be as nice as Barnum," Ben said.

The puppy cocked his head the other way.

"I'd *never* forget Barnum," Ben said firmly.

"But maybe I wouldn't have to," he said to himself as he looked at the eager puppy. "Maybe the puppy and I can remember Barnum together."

Ben looked at the puppy a long time. He looks as if he needs someone to love him, Ben thought, and I guess I need someone to love . . .

"I'll try," said Ben, and the puppy got so excited he chewed a pencil.

"Good morning, Mrs. Higgs," said Ben.

"Oh, no! Not another one!" said Mrs. Higgs. "And what sort of dog is *that*, may I ask?"

"A very special sort," said Ben, and he and Buster walked off down the road to the park.

The Hairy Dog

HERBERT ASQUITH

My dog's so furry I've not seen
His face for years and years.
His eyes are buried out of sight,
I only guess his ears.

When people ask me for his breed,
I do not know or care.
He has the beauty of them all
Hidden beneath his hair.

The Elephant's Trunk

AN AMERICAN FOLK RHYME

The elephant carries a great big trunk;
He never packs it with clothes;
It has no lock and it has no key,
But he takes it wherever he goes.

The Tale of the Clever Deer

A CHINESE FOLK TALE

A little deer was quietly nibbling some grass when all of a sudden a tiger jumped out of the nearby bushes. At the sight of the fierce tiger, the little deer's heart stood still with fear. But since there was no way to escape, he bravely stood his ground.

Now, ordinarily, the tiger would have eaten so small and tender an animal, but this tiger had never seen a deer before. "What are those things growing out of your head?" asked the tiger.

"Those are horns," said the little deer.

"Of what use are horns?" asked the tiger.

"Why, they are especially used to fork tigers," said the clever little deer.

"Really?" replied the tiger. "And what are all those white spots on your body?"

"Don't you know?" asked the little deer. "I thought everybody knew that. Each time I eat a tiger, a spot appears on my body. As you can see, I've eaten so many tigers that I'm practically covered with spots."

33

When the tiger heard this, he was so frightened that he bounded into the forest.

Soon he met a fox. He told the fox of the fearsome animal he had just met—the animal who forked tigers with his horns and who had eaten so many tigers.

"A little deer forking and eating tigers!" laughed the fox. "Oh, what a trick he has played on you!"

The tiger couldn't believe that the little deer had fooled him so completely. The fox said, "If you don't believe me, I'll show you myself. Just let me ride on your back and lead me to the deer. You'll soon see."

So they set out. When the little deer saw the tiger returning with the fox on his back, he knew at once that the fox had told the tiger the truth. He had to think fast to save himself, and think fast he did.

"Ho, there, friend fox!" he called. "I see you have kept your promise. You told me that you would bring me a fine tiger to eat, and that surely is a beauty you have there!"

When the tiger heard this, he needed no more convincing. He darted back into the forest—with the fox in his mouth! So the clever little deer was saved!

35

The Balancing Girl

BERNIECE RABE

Margaret was very good at balancing. She could balance a book on her head and glide along in her wheelchair. She could even balance herself and hop with her crutches. At school she balanced rows of felt-tip pens and built tall towers. Every time she finished a new work of art, Tommy Perkins would blurt out, "That's simple—anybody can do that!" Then he would knock Margaret's work over.

When the principal, Ms. Howard, announced that there would be a school carnival to raise money for gym equipment, Margaret began to plan. She wanted to make something that would raise lots of money. She also wanted it to be so special that Tommy couldn't call it simple and that he'd be sorry for knocking her things down.

Margaret made a private corner. In the farthest part of the corner, she started setting dominoes on end. Very gently, very carefully, she placed each domino just a small distance away from the last one. She had to be so very, very careful, for if even one little finger touched a domino and made it fall, then one by one they would all come toppling down.

She used up all the dominoes that belonged to Ms. Joliet's room. Ms. Joliet borrowed more from the second grade.

36

Margaret made fancy curves and snaky *S*'s. Ms. Joliet borrowed dominoes from the third grade.

Margaret made little stairs and let the dominoes march up and down them. Ms. Joliet said it was time for recess.

Tommy yelled dibs on the great big ball. He gave it two big bounces. It would have gone right into Margaret's domino corner if William hadn't jumped and caught it.

"Outside today!" said Ms. Joliet. She was careful to lock the room when they left.

The next day Margaret finished placing the last domino. Everyone begged and begged to be the one to push down the first domino. Even Tommy begged to be the one.

Margaret announced, "The name of the one to do that will be pulled out of a hat. *And* you will have to pay to get your name in that hat."

Ms. Joliet said, "The name will be drawn from the hat the last night of the school carnival."

Everyone clapped. Margaret was very happy and pleased. She was so happy she forgot to watch where her foot was. As she started to move out of the corner, her toe hit the end domino.

Click, click, click, click, click, click! Six dominoes fell down. But then they stopped. They had come to a corner. Oh, she had left too big a space. Thank goodness.

Gently, very, very, very gently, she put the six dominoes back upright. This time she made the space at the corner just perfect.

"O-h-h-h-h-h wow!" yelled the class.

"Don't scare me like that again!" said Ms. Joliet. "Class, you are all appointed guards of this corner from now until the end of the carnival."

That was one really great school carnival. The best part came when the loudspeaker announced, "Time for the

Grand Finale, folks. Let's move along to the first grade room and see who gets to push down that first domino."

There was lots of pushing and shoving, but Ms. Howard was good at waiting. She waited until everyone was gathered as close as possible to Margaret's corner. Then she let the oldest person in the room draw the name from the hat. Jannie's great-grandmother unfolded the paper and read, "Tommy Perkins."

Tommy pushed to the front of the crowd. He stepped inside the domino corner. He stood there for a long minute, looking at Margaret.

"Well, push," said Margaret.

Tommy pushed harder than was needed, but still it went beautifully. *Click, click, click,* a thousand times *click,* the dominoes took their turns falling. It seemed as though it took hours for them all to fall.

A big cheer went up!

And Tommy looked right at Margaret and yelled, "There! I knocked down something that you balanced, and I'm not sorry."

"I'm not sorry either," called back Margaret. "I made a hundred and one dollars and thirty cents—the most money in this carnival."

"Hurray for the Balancing Girl," someone shouted.

And Margaret was sure she heard Tommy join in with the big cheer that went up.

40

Unit Two
Nature

The Wind and the Sun

AESOP

Once the wind and the sun had a great quarrel. The wind said it was stronger than the sun. The sun said it was stronger than the wind. Each wished for some way to prove that it was the more powerful of the two.

Soon a man came along the road.

"Do you see that man?" asked the wind. "I can make him take off his coat."

"No, you cannot," said the sun, "but I can."

"We will both try," they said together. "We will see who is stronger."

The wind said it would try first. It blew as hard as it could. What a noise it made!

The man felt the wind blowing and said, "How cold it is!" Instead of taking off his coat, he pulled it more tightly around himself.

At last the wind said, "I cannot make the man take off his coat."

Then the sun tried. It made no noise. It shone hotter and hotter.

"How warm it is!" exclaimed the man. He took off
his coat.

"See what I did!" said the sun to the wind. "I made the
man take off his coat. That proves I am stronger than you."

Which do you think was stronger, the wind or the sun?

Fog

CARL SANDBURG

The fog comes
on little cat feet.

It sits looking
over harbor and city
on silent haunches
and then moves on.

April Rain Song

LANGSTON HUGHES

Let the rain kiss you.
Let the rain beat upon your head with silver liquid drops.
Let the rain sing you a lullaby.

The rain makes still pools on the sidewalk.
The rain makes running pools in the gutter.
The rain plays a little sleep-song on our roof at night—

And I love the rain.

Wind

BETTY MODARESSI

[PART 1]

Have you ever seen the wind blow? You may think you have, but you haven't. Wind is air that is moving, and air is invisible. You cannot see the wind, but you can see what the wind does.

Types of Winds

On some days you may think there is no wind at all. The leaves on the trees do not stir. When nothing seems to move, we say the air is *calm*. On other days you can see the leaves move gently. This kind of wind is called a *breeze*. At other times the wind is strong, and it makes large branches sway. Once in a while the wind is so strong that it causes branches, or even whole trees, to break. This very strong wind is called a *gale*. If you were outside during a gale, you might not be able to stand up. If you tried to walk in a gale, you might be blown away.

Causes of Wind

What causes wind? The sun heats the earth, which warms the air above it. Some parts of the earth heat faster than others. Warm air is light, and light things rise. Cooler air is heavier than warm air. Like all heavy things, the cooler air sinks.

As the air is heated, it rises. Cool air rushes into the space where the warm air was. Then the cool air is warmed by the land below it. It rises. More cool air rushes into the space where the warm air was. When you feel wind, that is warm air moving up and cool air rushing in to replace it.

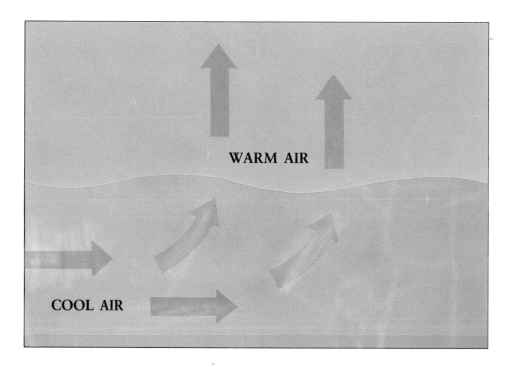

WARM AIR

COOL AIR

Walk barefoot along the beach near a large lake or an ocean on a warm day. The sun warms the sand or rocks along the shore more rapidly than it warms the water. You can notice the difference in temperatures by putting your feet in the water to cool them off.

As warm air above the shore rises, the cool air over the water rushes in to replace it. The rush of cool air is the breeze you can feel at the edge of the water.

[PART 2]

Types of Storms

An *air mass* is a large amount of air. There are cold air masses and warm air masses. When a warm air mass and a cold air mass meet, all kinds of weather changes take place.

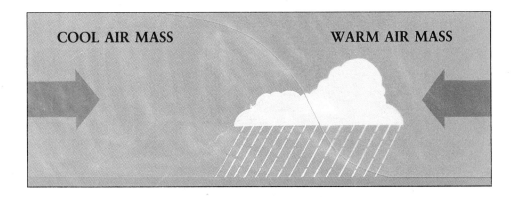

COOL AIR MASS   WARM AIR MASS

In winter when two masses meet, cold winds, a snowstorm, or a *blizzard* may take place. A blizzard is a snowstorm with very high winds and a very low temperature. It is the worst kind of winter storm.

A warm mass meeting a cold mass in summer may cause rain, warm winds, or a *tornado*. A tornado is one of the worst warm-weather storms. A tornado forms over land and is made of twisting winds that look like a giant funnel in the sky. Tornadoes are often called twisters.

Another bad warm-weather storm is a *hurricane*. It is made up of heavy rains and winds that spin very fast. A hurricane is much like a tornado, but it is larger and forms over an ocean. The center, or *eye*, of a hurricane is calm.

Blizzard   **Tornado**   **Hurricane**

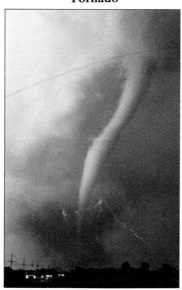

Effects of Wind

Winds can be both harmful and helpful. Wind is harmful when it blows down trees and buildings. It blows away soil from farmers' fields and even causes cars and airplanes to crash.

Wind is helpful in many ways. It spreads seeds and brings rain to help plants grow. It helps birds fly and clothes dry.

You can't see the wind, but you can feel it and see what it does. The next time you feel the wind, think about what causes it and the things it can do.

Who Has Seen the Wind?

CHRISTINA ROSSETTI

Who has seen the wind?
　Neither I nor you:
But when the leaves hang trembling,
　The wind is passing through.

Who has seen the wind?
　Neither you nor I:
But when the trees bow down their heads,
　The wind is passing by.

Wind Song

LILIAN MOORE

When the wind blows
The quiet things speak.
Some whisper, some clang,
Some creak.

Grasses swish.
Treetops sigh.
Flags slap
and snap at the sky.
Wires on poles
whistle and hum.
Ashcans roll.
Windows drum.

When the wind goes—
suddenly
then,
the quiet things
are quiet again.

51

Animal Fact, Animal Fable

SEYMOUR SIMON

Many of us like to watch animals. You may have a pet dog or cat. At times you may notice that your pet moves its tail one way when it's happy and a different way when it's angry. After watching your pet for a long time, you can probably tell a great deal about what each kind of tail movement means.

But even if you watch animals closely, it is sometimes easy to mistake what is happening. For example, a bat flutters around in an odd way in the night sky. Some people may think that bats are blind and can't see where they are going.

If bats are really blind, that belief is true; it is a fact. But suppose the bat flies in that odd way for another reason and is not really blind. Then the belief is a fable; it is not true.

On the next few pages, we'll look at some common beliefs about animals. You'll find out whether each belief is a fact or a fable. You'll also discover why scientists think the belief is a fact or a fable.

FACT OR FABLE?

An owl is a wise bird.

FABLE. Some people think an owl looks wise because of its wide-open eyes. But for a bird its size, the owl has a tiny brain. If you say a person is as wise as an owl, you are saying he or she is a birdbrain! An owl's eyes, though, are very sharp. It can see even small objects, such as mice, that are very far away.

FACT OR FABLE?

Crickets tell the temperature with their chirps.

FACT. Crickets are animals whose body temperatures change with the temperature around them. On a hot day, crickets chirp so rapidly that it is hard to count the number of chirps. But on a cool day, crickets chirp much more slowly. We can easily count the times they chirp.

Some people say they can use the number of chirps to find the exact temperature. That's not always possible. A cricket's chirping depends upon its age and health as well as on the temperature.

FACT OR FABLE?

Goats will eat almost anything.

FACT. Goats will eat almost anything they can find. They even seem to eat tin cans. But they are not really eating the metal can. They are chewing the label to get at the glue underneath.

Though goats eat string and paper, they would rather eat fruit, vegetables, grass, and leaves of plants. They are not quite the "garbage cans" some people think they are.

FACT OR FABLE?

Bats are blind.

FABLE. In the night sky, bats seem to be blind. They fly back and forth in odd ways. But they are really catching tiny flying insects in the air. You can't see the insects in the darkness. You can see only the strange twisting movements of the bat.

Bats use their ears as well as their eyes to find their way at night. Most kinds of bats squeak in short bursts of high-pitched sounds. The sounds echo back from objects to the bats' ears and help the bats to catch insects on the wing.

Benny's Animals

MILLICENT E. SELSAM

One day Benny went for a walk on the beach. He found many things. He put them in a paper bag.

When he got home, he took them out of the bag and looked at them.

Some looked like this.

Some looked like this.

A few looked like this.

And one looked like this.

Benny called to his mother. "Mother," he said, "do you know what these things are?"

"They are the shells of animals," said his mother.

"I did not know shells came from animals," said Benny.

"Well, they do," said his mother. "Some animals can take minerals from the sea water to build shells. This one is a clam. And this one is a scallop. I'm not sure what that round one is. Let's look it up."

She gave Benny a book with pictures of animals that live in the sea. Benny looked at the pictures. He found the round shell. It was a moon snail. And he found the shell with legs. It was a crab.

Benny went back to his room. He put all the clams in one pile. He put the scallops in another pile. He put the moon snails together. He kept the crab by itself. Then he made a sign: ANIMALS FROM THE SEA.

Benny's friend John came to see him. He looked at Benny's sign. "Why do you call these things animals?" he asked.

"Because they are animals," said Benny.

"That's not what I call an animal," said John.

"All right," said Benny, "what is an animal?"

"A horse is an animal," said John. "So is a zebra. And a cat. And an elephant. Animals all have heads and bodies and four legs."

"How about birds?" said Benny. "They only have two legs."

"Birds are birds, not animals," said John.

"How about fish?" asked Benny. "They have no legs at all."

"Fish are fish," said John. "I don't call them animals."

Then Benny asked, "How about a butterfly?"

"That I know," said John. "They are insects, not animals."

"But my mother said these clams and snails were animals," said Benny.

"Hmmmm," said John. "Let's go ask her again."

They went to Benny's mother. "Didn't you say my clams and snails were animals?" asked Benny.

"Yes," said Benny's mother. "Any living thing that is not a plant is an animal."

"So what is a living thing?" asked Benny.

"Well," said his mother, "our cat is a living thing. But a rock is not. Can you tell me how a rock is different from a cat?"

"A rock doesn't eat," said Benny.

"A rock can't grow," said John.

"A rock can't breathe," said Benny.

"Very good," said Benny's mother. "And a rock can't make more rocks like itself. Your clams and snails can do all of this, and they are not plants."

"So I guess they really are animals," said John.

"So my sign is right," said Benny.

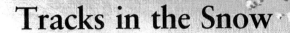

Tracks in the Snow

MARCHETTE CHUTE

This was a mouse who played around
All by himself one night,
Dancing under the winter moon
Forward and left and right.

This was a pheasant walking by,
Out with a friend or two—
This was a rabbit running fast,
The way rabbits do.

This was a squirrel who found a nut—
This was a chickadee—
And this uncommon sort of track
I think was probably me.

The Squirrel

ANONYMOUS

Whisky, frisky,
Hippity hop,
Up he goes
To the tree top!

Whirly, twirly,
Round and round,
Down he scampers
To the ground.

Furly, curly,
What a tail!
Tall as a feather,
Broad as a sail!

Where's his supper?
In the shell,
Snappity, crackity,
Out it fell!

Partners

BETTY BAKER

Long ago when all was new, everyone helped to make the world. Some dug rivers and canyons. Some pushed up dirt to make mountains and hills. Others made rocks and bright stones and sand, or planted trees and rolled out grass. Birds dropped seeds for plants and flowers.

Badger was putting the stars in the sky. The bag of stars was big and lumpy. The ladder was long.

But Badger was very strong. He was also neat and very careful. He put out the stars in the right order.

Everyone was helping make the world. Everyone but Coyote. Coyote was singing to the new moon.

Badger went by, pulling the bag and the long ladder.

Coyote said, "Is there something to eat in that bag?"

"No!" said Badger. "I do not eat now. There will be a dance when the world is finished. I will eat then."

"I will go to the dance with you," said Coyote.

Badger said, "Only those who help make the world will go to the dance."

Coyote did not like to dig or push dirt, but he wanted to go to the dance.

"You need a partner," he said to Badger. "You need a partner to move the ladder and hold it for you."

"I can do that myself," said Badger.

"Yes," said Coyote, "but if I do it, you can just think about the stars and how to put them."

"All right," said Badger. "You will be my partner."

He took some stars and went up the ladder. He put out the stars—one by one. Then he came down.

"Very pretty," said Coyote. "But make it bigger."

He moved the ladder. Up went Badger. Up went the stars—one by one.

"That is bigger," said Coyote. "But use more stars."

Badger went up the ladder again. He was up there a long time. He used a lot of stars, and he put them out—one by one.

"Can't you do it faster?" said Coyote.

"No," said Badger. "The sky must be neat. The stars must go up in the right order."

Again and again, Coyote moved the ladder. Again and again, Badger went up and put the stars out—one by one.

The digging was finished. The mountains and hills had trees and flowers. But Badger still was putting up stars.

Coyote could smell the food cooking. "Hurry," said Coyote. "We will miss the dance."

But Badger put the stars out—one by one.

The bag of stars was still almost full. Coyote took the
bag. He told Badger, "A partner should make things easy
for you. I will show you a better way." And he threw the
stars all over the sky.

"The sky is a mess!" said Badger.

"But we are finished," said Coyote. "Now we can go to the dance."

And they did.

Coyote told everyone, "Badger and I are partners. We put up the stars. Badger put up the pretty ones, but I put up the most." Then he ate and sang and danced and ate.

But Badger dug a hole in the ground so he would not see the messy sky.

67

A Story of a Turnip

A FOLK TALE

One day a poor farmer found a large turnip in her garden. "I will take this turnip to the king," she said, "and offer it to him as a gift. He is always glad when we have good crops in our gardens and fields."

So the farmer carried the turnip to the castle. The king took it and admired its great size and beauty. Then he said some kind words to the poor woman and gave her three gold pieces.

Near the village of the poor farmer lived another farmer. He was very rich, and he always wanted to be richer. He heard about the kindness that the king had shown to the poor farmer and about the money he had given her.

"I have a big calf," said he, "the largest and finest calf in the country. I will take it to the king and offer it as a gift. If he gave three gold pieces for a turnip, how much more will he give for a beautiful calf!"

So he tied a rope around the calf's neck and led it to the castle.

"My good king," he said, "here is a calf which I have fed and brought up with great care. I want to show my love for you by offering it to you as a gift. Please take it with my best wishes."

But the king understood what was in the mind of the farmer, and he said that he did not want the calf. The man begged the king to take the gift. He would never be happy, he said, if he should have to take the calf back home.

"Very well," said the wise king, "since you wish me to do so, I will take it. In order that you may know how much I think of you, I will give you a present that cost me at least three times as much as your calf is worth."

Saying these words, he gave the farmer the big turnip that had led to this gift giving. The farmer, as he went sadly home, thought that he had done a very foolish thing.

The Emperor's New Clothes

HANS CHRISTIAN ANDERSEN

Many years ago there lived an emperor who cared more for clothes than for anything else in the world. He had a different outfit for every hour of the day, and he spent most of his time changing from one outfit into another. He was so busy changing clothes that when anyone wanted to see him, the servants would always say, "The emperor is in his dressing room."

One day two strangers, who were not as honest as they should have been, came to the emperor's city. They claimed to be weavers. "The cloth we weave," they said, "is very beautiful and quite out of the ordinary. It cannot be seen by people who are foolish or who are not fit for their jobs."

"Well!" said the emperor when he heard of these unusual weavers. "I must have some clothes made from this remarkable cloth. What a chance to find out which of my people are fit for their work and which of them are fools!" He gave the strangers a great deal of money and ordered them to weave their cloth for him.

The two rascals set up their looms. They asked for the finest silk and pure-gold thread. The silk and thread went into their own bags, and the looms remained empty, as they sat pretending to weave.

After some time the emperor decided to go see how the weavers were getting along with the unusual cloth. He found them sitting at their empty looms, seeming to be hard at work.

"Oh, your majesty," the weavers exclaimed, "isn't this beautiful cloth? Have you ever seen such colors? And such a pattern!"

"Good heavens!" said the emperor to himself. "I can't see a thing! Can it be that I am foolish? Am I not fit to be emperor? Well, I would never have thought so. Nobody else had better think it either!" So he made admiring noises and said aloud, "How splendid! It is just as beautiful as you said." He gave each of the weavers a medal to wear and the title Knight of the Loom.

"Why not wear a suit made from this wonderful cloth in the parade next week?" asked one of his ministers.

"That's a splendid idea," said the emperor.

All through the night before the parade, the weavers kept many candles burning. People could see how busy they were, finishing off the emperor's new clothes. The weavers pretended to take the cloth from the looms. They clipped away at the air with huge scissors. They stitched and stitched, using needles without any thread. "See," they cried at last, just as the sun came up, "the emperor's new clothes are ready!"

When the emperor arrived with all of his court, the weavers lifted their arms, as if they were holding up something to show him. "Here are your trousers, your Majesty. And this is the coat! And the cape! Let us help you put them on. See, the cloth is as light as a spider's web. You might almost think you had nothing on!"

"Beautiful, indeed," murmured everyone, though not a single person could see anything at all. The emperor's servants busied themselves pretending to hold up the ends of the new cape. The emperor turned around and around in front of the mirror, admiring himself.

Then he marched down the street at the head of the parade. All the people of the city looked at him and said,

"Beautiful! Magnificent!" No one wanted to be thought foolish or unfit to serve the emperor. Never before had the emperor's clothes been such a success.

The emperor held his head high and felt very proud as he marched along. The two weavers laughed to themselves to think how easy it was to make people look silly.

Suddenly a little girl's voice rose over the others. "But he has nothing on!" she cried.

The girl's words were whispered from person to person in the crowd. "Did you hear that? There's a child saying he has nothing on!"

Soon everyone began to whisper and then to shout, *"But he has nothing on!"*

Then the emperor felt very foolish indeed, for he knew the people were right. But what could he do about it now? He held his head up still more proudly and marched on, while his servants walked after him, carrying the cape that wasn't there.

Unit Three
Work and Play

Discovering Dinosaurs

CHARNAN SIMON

You have seen pictures of them. You have probably played with models of them. You may even have seen their bones in a museum. But nobody has ever seen real, live dinosaurs. Nobody ever will.

Millions of years ago, dinosaurs lived all over the earth. They lived on every continent. Some were as long as a football field. Others were no bigger than a chicken. Some ate meat, and some ate plants. Some walked on land, while others swam in the sea. For almost 140 million years, dinosaurs roamed the world.

Then, about 65 million years ago, the dinosaurs all died out, or became *extinct*. Nobody really knows why they became extinct. The weather may have become too cold for them. Maybe they couldn't get enough to eat. Perhaps other animals ate the dinosaurs' eggs. If that happened, there would be no young dinosaurs to grow up and take the place of older dinosaurs when they died. Or perhaps something terrible happened to the earth. Maybe a huge volcano blew up. There may have been a great flood, or even a big explosion in the sky. We just don't know.

All we do know is that 65 million years ago, all the dinosaurs disappeared. But here is a puzzle. No human being has ever seen living dinosaurs. Then how do we know so much about them?

Here is what happened. When the dinosaurs died, many of them just rotted away. Some of them, however, were covered with the sand and mud. They were buried that way for millions of years. The skin and meat of these dinosaurs did rot away, but the bones were preserved by the sand and mud. The sand and mud with the dinosaurs' bones turned into rock, and these dinosaur bones became what we call *fossils*.

The first dinosaur fossil was found by accident in 1822.

After that, many people went looking for fossils. They found dinosaur bones and dinosaur teeth and even dinosaur eggs. By carefully studying these fossils, people learned a great deal about the creatures we call dinosaurs.

The people who study fossils are called *paleontologists*. A paleontologist is a scientist who studies plants and animals that lived long ago.

Looking for fossils is hard work. Many people must work together to do the job. First they must choose a likely site for digging. Fossils are often found in hot, dry places. They are often far away from town and cities. This means that the fossil hunters have to camp out while they do their digging.

The workers use shovels, picks, and sometimes even their hands to dig out fossils. They must work very carefully so that they do not hurt the fossils. It is especially hard work because fossils are often buried in solid rock. The workers must then chip away the rock from around the fossils very slowly and carefully.

After digging out a fossil, the paleontologist numbers each piece, packs it carefully, and takes it to a museum. At the museum, experts clean the fossil bones and teeth. They repair any that are broken. Then they may put the bones together to make a skeleton—or part of one.

Paleontologists hardly ever find all the bones of a dinosaur. They may make the missing bones out of plaster or plastic. It is like working out a giant jigsaw puzzle. Sometimes it takes the museum workers years to put together just one dinosaur!

Paleontologists can tell a great deal about a dinosaur by studying its fossils. By studying its bones, they can tell about how big it was. They can also tell whether the dinosaur was good at swimming or walking or even flying. By studying its teeth, they can tell whether the animal ate meat or plants.

No human being has ever seen a living dinosaur, and no one ever will. We have seen the fossil clues that dinosaurs left behind, though. Thanks to fossils, we know a great deal about the way these amazing creatures lived millions and millions of years ago.

He Started Out as a Child

ELIZABETH WASHBURN

William is bright and well liked, but he spends too much of his time clowning around. He should do well in every subject, but his work is careless, and his study habits are poor.

More often than not Bill Cosby's teachers wrote reports like the one above. From the fourth or fifth grade on, Bill seemed more interested in entertaining his classmates than in studying. In the tenth grade he dropped out of school and joined the navy. He completed high school during his four years in the navy and decided that education was really important to him after all. He has since graduated from college and has gone on to even higher education.

Bill Cosby was born and grew up in north Philadelphia. He remembers being very poor and working at several different jobs to make money for his family. His life was not easy, but Bill had many friends and a sense of humor.

Some of his funniest stories are about the kids in his neighborhood—Fat Albert, Weird Harold, Dumb Donald, to name a few—and about his childhood.

His career as a comic started after he got out of the navy and was going to college at Temple University. He was on the track and football teams and worked in a coffeehouse in Philadelphia to make extra money for college. He was paid five dollars a night to wait on customers and tell jokes. He was so funny that soon he was offered other jobs in night clubs and, finally, in television and the movies.

Although Bill Cosby isn't a kid any more—he even has children of his own—he still remembers what it was like to be one. He likes talking to kids and making them laugh. Through television—"The Bill Cosby Show" and his appearances on "The Electric Company"—Bill has reached many boys and girls and their parents.

Bill believes very strongly in education and encourages boys and girls to stay in school. By talking to kids about school and about their problems, he makes important contributions to the field of education.

Emma

WENDY KESSELMAN

[PART 1]

It was Emma's birthday. She was seventy-two years old.

Emma had four children, seven grandchildren, and fourteen great-grandchildren.

Emma was happy when her family came to visit. She baked noodle puddings and chocolate cream pies. She put flowers everywhere.

Her family brought her lots of presents, but they never stayed very long. So most of the time Emma was all alone. Sometimes she was very lonely. The only company she had was her orange cat, Pumpkinseed. They sat together outside and curled their toes in the sun. They listened to the woodpecker tapping at the old apple tree.

Sometimes Pumpkinseed got stuck at the top of the tree, and Emma had to climb up and rescue him. Emma didn't mind. She loved climbing trees.

She loved all kinds of simple things. She loved to see the snow come right up to her doorstep. She loved to sit and dream about the little village across the mountains where she had grown up.

But when she told her family about the things she loved, they laughed and said to each other, "Poor Emma. She must be getting old."

For her seventy-second birthday the family gave Emma a painting of her little village across the mountains.

Emma hung the painting on the wall. "It's beautiful," she said to them. To herself she said, "That's not how I remember my village at all."

Every day Emma looked at the painting and frowned.

Every day her frown grew a little deeper.

One day she made up her mind. She went to the store and bought paints and brushes and an easel.

Then Emma sat by the window and painted her village just the way she remembered it. When it was finished she took the other painting off the wall and hung hers up instead. Every day Emma looked at her painting and smiled.

When her family came to visit, Emma put the other painting back again. As soon as they left she switched it for her own.

[PART 2]

One day Emma forgot to switch the paintings. When the family was in the middle of dinner, one of Emma's grandchildren pointed to the wall. "Where did that painting come from? It's not the one we gave you!"

Emma looked up. Emma looked down. Everyone else kept right on looking at the painting, and they all kept asking, "Yes, where did it come from?"

Finally Emma said, "Me," very softly. "*I* did it."

"*You!*" they all cried out together.

Emma hurried to hide the painting in the closet.

"Stop!" cried her family. "Don't hide it away!" "It's beautiful! Why don't you paint another one?"

"I have," said Emma. She brought twenty more paintings out of the closet.

From that day Emma kept painting, and she never stopped. She painted the snow coming right up to her doorstep. She painted the old apple tree in blossom with the woodpecker tapping at its branches. She painted Pumpkinseed curling his toes in the sun. And she painted her village across the mountains over and over and over again.

Soon people began coming from everywhere to look at Emma's paintings. When they left, she was all alone.

But now Emma had something else. She sat by the window every day and painted from morning till night. She painted hundreds of paintings. Her paintings covered the walls. They filled the closets. They hung in the kitchen cupboards.

Emma was surrounded by the friends and places she loved. And she was never lonely again.

The Bremen Town Musicians

JACOB and WILHELM GRIMM

[PART 1]

Once upon a time there lived an old donkey who had carried many a heavy sack of grain to the mill for his master. Now he was worn out and weary and could work no more. His master wanted to get him out of the way. The donkey said to himself, "An ill wind is blowing! I had better get out of here while I can still use my four legs." And he started out for the town of Bremen, thinking that he might become a town musician to make a living.

He had not gone very far when he came upon a big hunting dog who panted like one too tired to go one step farther. "Now, now, old hound," said the donkey, "why are you panting so hard?"

"Ach," said the dog sadly, "I am old and getting weaker every day. I am not fit any more to go hunting with my master, and that's why he wanted to kill me. But I took to my heels and here I am. A lot of good it does me now, not knowing how to earn my food!"

"I have an idea, good friend," said the donkey. "I am on my way to Bremen, and there I plan to become a town musician. Come along with me and take up music too! I'll play the lute and you can pound the drum." The dog was content with this plan, and the two traveled on together.

Before long they met a cat whose face looked as sad and long as a three-day rain. "Well, old Whisker-wiper, what has crossed your path today?" asked the donkey.

"Who can be cheerful when his life is at stake?" answered the cat. "I am getting on in years, my teeth are no longer sharp, and I find it easier to sit by the fire and dream than to run after mice. That's why my mistress wanted to drown me. I ran away and here I am, but what shall I do now?"

"Come along with us," said the donkey. "We are going to Bremen to be musicians. You surely have talent for singing at night, so you can become a town musician like us." The cat liked the idea and joined them.

Soon the three runaways came to a farmyard. There on top of the gate sat a rooster, crowing away at the top of his lungs. "You crow loud enough to pierce our bones and marrow," said the donkey. "What's up?"

"My mistress told the cook to put me in the soup for Sunday dinner tomorrow. My head will be cut off tonight.

So I am crowing at the top of my voice as long as I am still able."

"Now, now, Redhead," said the donkey, "you'll find something better than death anywhere! Why don't you travel with us to Bremen and be a musician? You have a fine lusty voice, and when the four of us are making music together, it will be something to listen to!" The rooster agreed, and so all four of them traveled on together.

Toward evening they came to a forest where they decided to spend the night. The donkey and the dog lay down under a big tree, the cat climbed to the lower branches, and the rooster flew up to the very top. Just before he closed his eyes, however, the rooster took a long look in all four directions. All of a sudden he saw a tiny light glowing among the trees. "I can see a light," he shouted down to his companions. "There has to be a house not far away!"

"We must get up and go there," said the donkey. "These quarters are none too comfortable."

So they started out toward the light, which became bigger and bigger, until at last they found themselves in front of a brightly lit house of robbers. Looking inside, they saw a table covered with delicious food and drink. The robbers were sitting around the table, having a good time.

"That would be just the thing for us!" said the rooster.

"Oh my, yes, if only we could be sitting in there," replied the donkey.

The animals put their heads together and came up with a plan to chase the robbers away. The donkey stood at the window with his forefeet on the ledge. The dog jumped on the donkey's back, the cat climbed on the dog's back, and finally the rooster flew up and perched himself on top of the cat. This done, the donkey gave a signal, and they all started to make their music—as loud as they possibly could. The donkey brayed, the dog barked, the cat meowed, and the rooster crowed! Then they burst through the window right into the middle of the room, the glass crashing and clattering all around them. The robbers, not knowing what had broken into their house, jumped up and fled, terror-stricken, far into the forest.

The four musicians sat down at the table and ate as though they had to eat enough for four weeks. Then they blew out the light, and each one looked for a place to sleep. The donkey went outside and lay down on top of a pile of hay. The dog stretched out behind the back door. The cat curled up on the hearth next to the warm ashes, and the rooster perched himself on top of the roof. All four soon were fast asleep.

Some time after midnight the robbers came out from their hiding place in the woods. Everything seemed quiet and safe. The robber chief said, "We should not have let ourselves get frightened so easily." He ordered one of the robbers to go to the house and look around.

The robber did as he was told and, finding everything peaceful and quiet, went to the kitchen to light a lamp. Mistaking the glowing, fiery eyes of the cat for live coals, he tried to light his match from them. But the cat did not think this a joke and sprang right into his face, spitting and scratching. The robber, frightened out of his wits, started to run out of the back door, but the dog, who lay there, leaped up and bit him in the leg.

When the robber ran past the hay pile, the donkey gave him a hearty kick with his hind hoof. And the rooster, who

had been awakened by all this noise and thought it was morning, lustily crowed, "Keekerikee! Keekerikee!" The terrified robber ran as though his life depended on it and did not stop until he reached his chief.

"What horrors!" he gasped. "In the house by the fire sits a dreadful witch. She hissed at me and scratched my face with her long fingernails. In front of the door stands a man with a knife, and he stabbed my leg as I ran out. In the yard lurks a black monster that beat me with a wooden club. Up on the roof sits the judge, and he screamed, 'Keep the thief here! Keep the thief here!' That was too much for me, and I took to my heels."

From then on none of the robbers ever dared to go back to the house or even come near it. The four town musicians, however, liked their new home so well that they lived in it happy and contented for the rest of their lives.

Blum

DOROTHY ALDIS

Dog means dog. And cat means cat.
And there are lots of words like that.

A cart's a cart to pull or push.
A leaf's a leaf on tree or bush.

But there's another word I say
When I am left alone to play.

The word is Blum. Blum is a word
That very few have ever heard.

It is very nice to hum.
Or you can shout it: BLUM BLUM BLUM.

But shout or whisper, hum or sing,
It doesn't mean a single thing.

Gwendolyn Brooks

VALJEAN McLENIGHAN

Flames swept through the building on Chicago's South Side. People poured into the street to watch the building burn. The fire drew them like a magnet.

Keziah Brooks rushed to her daughter's room. "Gwendolyn, there's a big fire down the street!"

"Yes, I know," said the girl. She did not look up from her desk.

Gwendolyn wrote at her desk every day. Once she started writing, almost nothing could disturb her. Her family and neighbors ran to watch the fire. Sirens sounded as fire fighters battled the flames. But Gwendolyn Brooks stayed in her room. She was working on her latest poem.

Gwendolyn spent most of her time alone, writing stories and poems. She liked to work at home where her family was warm and loving. Gwendolyn's father read to his family every day. Her mother had been a teacher. She encouraged Gwendolyn's love for reading and writing.

Gwendolyn started writing poems when she was seven years old. She was only thirteen when her first poem was published in a magazine. Later she showed her work to the great black poets James Weldon Johnson and Langston Hughes. They told her she had talent and urged her to keep writing.

Gwendolyn did continue to write. More than seventy of her poems were published while she was still a teen-ager. Her first book of poems was called *A Street in Bronzeville*. This book was about the pains and joys of poor black people. Many more books of Gwendolyn's poems have been published over the years.

Today, Gwendolyn Brooks is a world-famous poet. She has won many honors and awards. Most of her poems are about the everyday life of black people, but her work has something to say to everyone.

Gwendolyn still writes almost every day. She also visits schools to talk with students about poetry. Often she reads

her poems aloud. She encourages young people to write, in the same way that others encouraged her.

Beginning in September 1985, Gwendolyn spent a year working at the Library of Congress in Washington, D.C. The Library of Congress serves as our country's national library. Gwendolyn's job there was very important. She gave advice about the poetry books in the library's collection. She planned special events and programs for people who visited the library. Perhaps best of all, she gave public readings of her own poems in our country's capital city. And Gwendolyn Brooks's poems are so good that, when she reads them aloud, not even fire sirens disturb her listeners!

Cynthia in the Snow

GWENDOLYN BROOKS

It SUSHES.
It hushes
The loudness in the road.
It flitter-twitters,
And laughs away from me.
It laughs a lovely whiteness,
And whitely whirs away,
To be
Some otherwhere,
Still white as milk or shirts.
So beautiful it hurts.

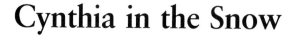

Tommy

GWENDOLYN BROOKS

I put a seed into the ground
And said, "I'll watch it grow."
I watered it and cared for it
As well as I could know.

One day I walked in my back yard,
And oh, what did I see!
My seed had popped itself right out,
Without consulting me.

Sam

ANN HERBERT SCOTT

Sam wanted to play. Everyone in his house was busy, and no one wanted to play with him.

Sam walked into the kitchen, where his mother was peeling apples for pie. He picked up a knife from the table.

"SAM, don't touch that knife," cried his mother. "That knife is very sharp—too sharp for little boys. I don't ever want to see you touch that knife again."

Sam's mother went back to peeling apples. "Why don't you go outside and play, Sammy," she said.

Sam walked out on the porch. His big brother George was sitting on the steps, reading his books from school. Sam picked up a book and turned the pages to find a picture.

"SAM, put down that book," yelled George. "That's *my* book, and you're not to touch it."

Sam looked as if he might cry.

"That's a book I got from school," said George, not quite so loudly as before. "If you get it dirty or rip the pages, I'll be in trouble. Don't ever touch my books again. Understand?"

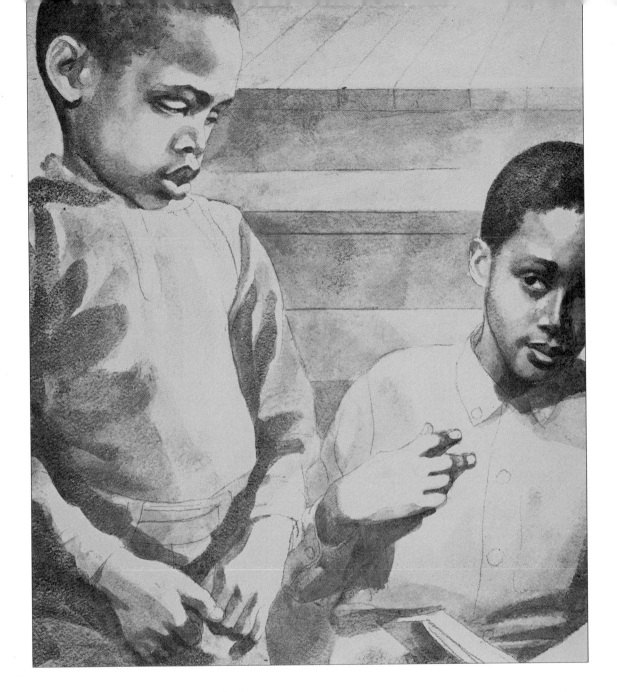

Sam just stood there.

"Why don't you go inside and play, Sammy,"
said George.

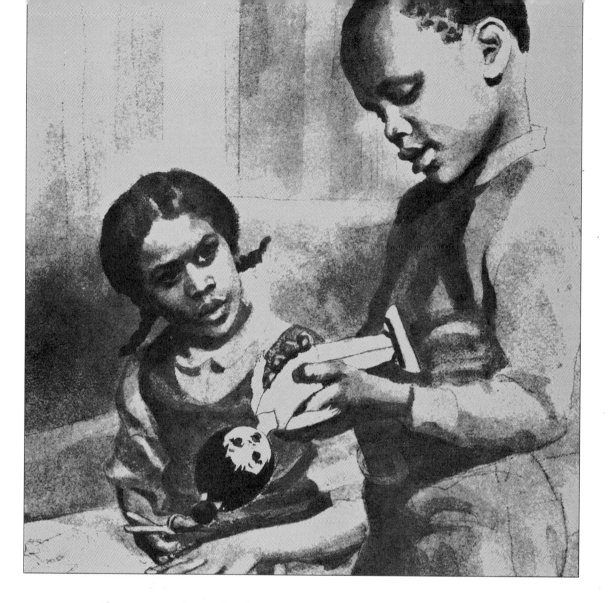

Sam went into the living room. There by the window
his big sister Marcia was making clothes for her paper dolls.
Sam picked up one of the dolls and waved its hand up
and down.

"SAM," screamed Marcia when she saw what he was
doing. "You'll bend my doll's hand. You'll *ruin* her!"

Sam looked as if he might cry.

"You go play somewhere else, Sammy. But don't ever touch my dolls again."

Sam just stood there.

"Why don't you go find Daddy," said Marcia.

Sam's father was sitting at his desk, reading the newspaper. Sam stood beside him for a minute. Then PING, Sam punched down a key on the typewriter.

"SAM, get your hands off that typewriter," shouted his father. "How many times must I tell you—that typewriter is not a toy for children. Typewriters are very easy to break and they cost lots of money to fix. Don't ever touch my typewriter again."

Sam's father turned back to his newspaper. "Why don't you go find Mother," he said.

Then Sam really did cry. He sat right down on the floor by his father's desk, and he cried and cried and cried.

He cried so loudly that his mother came in from the kitchen, and his big brother George came in from the porch, and his big sister Marcia came in from the living room.

"What in the world is the matter with Sam?" asked his father.

"I think I know," said his mother, sitting down in the rocking chair by the desk and picking up Sam in her arms.

"I think I know, too," said George.

"I think I know, too," said Marcia.

For a minute everyone was quiet. The rocking chair creaked back and forth as Sam curled in his mother's arms.

"Sammy," said his mother, "if you're not too busy, there's a job you could do for me in the kitchen."

Sam was tired of crying, so he followed his mother into the kitchen. His father and his big sister and his big brother all came along, too.

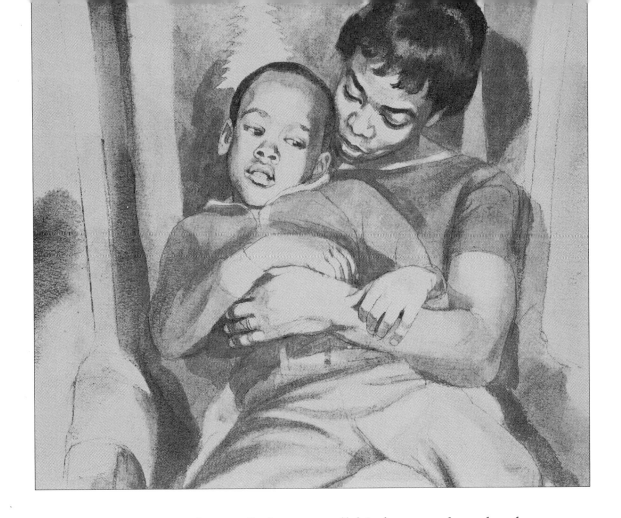

Sam's mother pulled out a tall kitchen stool so that he could reach the table. Then she pinned a dish towel around his neck so that he wouldn't get dirty. And then she gave him a piece of soft pie dough and a rolling pin so that he could roll the dough out flat.

"There's just enough dough to fit in this little pan," said Sam's mother. "Maybe you can make a tart to bake in the oven with the pie."

"Say, that's a good job for Sam," said his father.

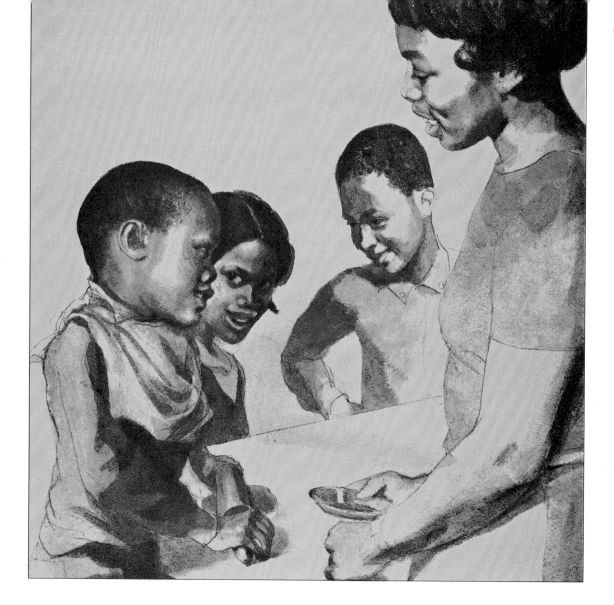

"He's not too little," said his sister.

"And he's not too big," said his brother.

"In fact," said his mother, "he's just the right size. And now, Sammy, what kind of jam would you like for your tart?"

"Raspberry," said Sam.

The Ants and the Grasshopper

AESOP

Once on a lovely summer's day a grasshopper was hopping about in a field. It was dancing and singing and chirping to its heart's content.

The grasshopper came upon some ants working very hard to gather food to take to their nest.

"Good day," said the grasshopper. "Why not stop and talk with me instead of working so hard?"

"We must work," said the ants. "We must store up food for the winter. You would be wise to do the same."

"Winter is a long way off," said the grasshopper. "We all have enough food to eat. Come and enjoy this lovely day."

But the ants went on their way and continued to work.

By and by, winter came. The days were cold, and the long grass was stiff with frost. The birds had gone away to their winter homes.

The grasshopper had no food and was too weak and hungry to dance or sing or chirp.

The ants, however, were eating well enough. Every day the grasshopper saw them passing out corn and grain from the stores they had gathered in the summer.

"Please give me some food," the grasshopper said to the ants. "I am very hungry."

"We're sorry, but we have only enough food for ourselves," said the ants, and they turned the grasshopper away.

Then, when it was too late, the grasshopper knew what it should have done in the summer.

The Elves and the Shoemaker

JACOB and WILHELM GRIMM

Once upon a time there lived a shoemaker. This shoemaker worked very hard, but he could not earn enough money to live on. All he had left was one piece of leather, which was just enough to make one pair of shoes.

He cut out the shoes in the evening and left them on his bench, meaning to stitch them up early in the morning. He was a good man, and his heart was light in spite of his troubles, so he went peacefully off to sleep.

In the morning the shoemaker was up early and sat down at his bench to work. To his great surprise, the shoes were standing on the table, already made. He rubbed his eyes and wondered if he were dreaming. He picked the

shoes up and looked at them closely. They were so neatly made that not a tiny stitch was out of place. Better still, in came a customer who was so pleased with the shoes that he paid a high price for them.

Now the shoemaker had money to buy leather for two pairs of shoes. He cut the shoes out in the evening, meaning to finish them in the morning. He was spared the trouble, though—for when he got up, there were two pairs of shoes on the table, as perfectly made as the first. That same day two customers came in and paid the shoemaker so well for his shoes that he could buy enough leather for four pairs of shoes.

And so it went. The shoes the shoemaker cut out in the evening were always finished by morning. The good man's troubles were over.

One evening, not long before Christmas, when he had cut out the shoes as usual, he said to his wife, "Suppose we sit up and watch tonight to find out who has been helping us?"

"Yes, indeed!" agreed his wife.

They left a candle burning, hid themselves behind a curtain in the corner of the room, and waited to see what would happen.

Just as the clock struck twelve, two tiny elves came

dancing into the room. They hopped up onto the bench, took up the leather and began to stitch and sew and hammer at such a rate that the shoemaker and his wife couldn't believe their eyes. On and on the elves worked until all of the shoes lay finished on the table. Then they were gone as suddenly as they had come.

"Well!" said the shoemaker's wife. "Did you see those poor little things? Hardly a rag on their backs, and shivering with the cold! They've been very good to us. I'm going to make shirts and trousers and coats for them, and I'll knit them each a pair of warm stockings as well."

"A good idea!" replied the shoemaker. "And I will make each of them a little pair of shoes."

They set to work that very day. The wife cut out and stitched two fine white shirts, two tiny coats, and two little pairs of trousers. Then she knitted two pairs of stockings. The shoemaker made two small pairs of bright red shoes with turned-up toes. Everything was ready by evening. They laid all of the clothes and the shoes on the bench in place of the leather. Then they hid themselves away to see what the elves would do.

On the stroke of midnight the elves came skipping in. When they saw the clothes they laughed and jumped about with glee. They caught up the clothes and shoes, and put them on as quick as a wink. Then they began to sing. As they sang, they danced. As the first rays of sunlight found their way into the room, the elves danced out the door, over the green hills, and out of sight.

The elves never came back, but all went well with the shoemaker and his wife from then on, and they were known far and wide as the luckiest people in the land.

Unit Four
Think Again

The Camel's Nose

AN ARAB FABLE

One cold night an Arab was sitting inside his tent. Suddenly the Arab's camel stuck its nose under the flap of the tent and said, "Master, be good enough to let me put my head inside the tent, for it is cold outside."

"Very well," said the Arab, "you may put your head inside my tent."

So the camel put its head into the tent. Then in a little while the camel said, "Good master, pray let me put my neck into the tent also. I may catch a chill if my head is warm and my neck is cold."

"Very well," replied the Arab, "you may put your neck into the tent, too."

After a little while the camel said again, "Kind master, allow me to put my forelegs into the tent. They take up only a little room, and it is uncomfortable standing this way."

"Very well," said the Arab, "you may do so." The Arab moved over to make room for the camel, for the tent was very small.

Then in a little while more the camel said, "Generous

master, permit me to stand all the way inside the tent. I keep the flap of the tent open standing this way, and the cold air rushes inside."

"Very well, then," said the Arab. "You may come all the way inside."

The camel crowded its way into the tent, but the tent was too small for both man and camel.

"I think that there is not room for both of us in the tent," said the camel. "Since you are smaller than I, it would be better if you stood outside."

With these words the camel gave its master a little push. Soon the Arab found himself standing outside in the cold, while the camel was enjoying the warmth of the tent.

As the Arab stood shivering from the cold, he said to himself, "I can see now that it is better to stop bad things before they get started."

Mexicali Soup

KATHRYN HITTE and WILLIAM D. HAYE
Adapted by CHARNAN SIMON

CHARACTERS

MARIA	ANTONIO	MANUEL	ROSITA
MARJORIE	JUAN	MAMA	PAPA

[ACT I]

SCENE: *A city street.* MARIA *and* MARJORIE *are playing on the right.* ANTONIO *is standing by a table in the center, stacking vegetables.* JUAN *and* MANUEL *are playing to the left.* MAMA *comes in from the right, carrying a shopping bag.*

MAMA: What a lovely day! And what a lovely city! It isn't much like our old home in the mountains, but I like it anyway. But now I must do my shopping, for tonight will be a very special supper for my Rosita and Antonio and Juan and Manuel and Maria—and for Papa too. A very special supper of my Mexicali Soup, filled with potatoes and peppers, tomatoes and onions, garlic and

118

celery—all cooked together. (*She hums as she walks to where* MARIA *and* MARJORIE *are playing.*)

MARIA: Mama, wait a minute! Please, may I play at Marjorie's house this afternoon?

MAMA: Very well, for a while. But do not be late for supper, Maria. I am making my special Mexicali Soup tonight.

MARIA: Mmmm—Mexicali Soup! But Mama, there are such a lot of potatoes in your Mexicali Soup. City people like Marjorie and her family don't eat so many potatoes. We are city people now too. Could you please leave out the potatoes?

MAMA: No potatoes? Well, there are lots of good things in Mexicali Soup without potatoes.

MARIA: Thank you, Mama. You make the best soup in the world! (MARIA *and* MARJORIE leave.)

MAMA: Now I must hurry to Mr. Fernandez's market. That is where Antonio works and where I will get the most beautiful vegetables in the world! (MAMA *goes to* ANTONIO's *vegetable stand and picks out vegetables. She puts them in her sack.*)

ANTONIO: Hello, Mama. Let me help you. I hope you want something very good for our supper.

MAMA: Ah, *si*! For tonight we have Mexicali Soup!

ANTONIO: That's great! But, Mama, you use too many hot peppers in your soup. People here in the city don't cook that way. Please don't buy any peppers today.

MAMA: No peppers? Well, there are plenty of good things in the soup without peppers.

ANTONIO: Of course there are! Everyone knows you make the best soup in the world.

MAMA (*walking away from* ANTONIO): Well, well, a new kind of Mexicali Soup, for a new city.

JUAN and MANUEL: Mama! Mamacita! Wait for us!

JUAN (*looking in* MAMA's *bag*): Mmmm—tomatoes and celery—I know what that means.

MANUEL: Me, too. Onions and garlic—Mexicali Soup, right? But, Mama, you use an awful lot of onions. They have different ways of doing things here. I think we should try the new ways. Mamacita, please make the Mexicali Soup without onions.

JUAN: Manuel is right. I think there may be better ways of making our soup. Leave out the tomatoes, Mama!

MAMA: No tomatoes? And no onions? In Mexicali Soup? Well, well, it will be a new way, all right!
(MAMA *walks offstage.*)

JUAN: We will be hungry for your soup tonight.

MANUEL: You make the best soup in the world, Mamacita!

[ACT II]

SCENE: *The kitchen.* MAMA *is standing by a table putting groceries away.*

MAMA: Let's see, now. No potatoes, and no peppers. No tomatoes. No onions. Now what does that leave for Mexicali Soup?

(ROSITA *comes in.*)

ROSITA: Oh, Mama, I hope I'm in time! The boys and Maria—they all told me—and Mama! I want to ask you—please! No garlic! Just leave out the garlic, and you will make the best city soup in the world!

(PAPA *and the rest of the children come in.*)

PAPA: I hear we are having Mexicali Soup tonight, Mama. You make the best soup in the world!

MAMA: Ah, *si*! But you want me to leave out something? The celery, perhaps?

PAPA: Celery? What is celery? It is a little nothing. Put it in or leave it out, Mamacita. It does not matter. The soup will be just as—

MAMA: Enough! Out of my kitchen, all of you!

ROSITA: But, Mama, we always help you cook.

MAMA: No! Out! I am busy now! I will call you! Go!

(MAMA *shoos the family away, looking angry.*)

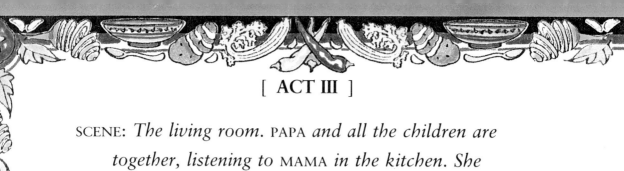

[ACT III]

SCENE: *The living room.* PAPA *and all the children are together, listening to* MAMA *in the kitchen. She is humming.*

PAPA: There now, you see? Mama is not angry. She was just tired from all her shopping. Listen to her humming. That shows that she is happy.

MAMA *(calling from the kitchen)*: The soup is finished. Come and eat now!

PAPA: Ah! That is what I like to hear. The soup is ready before I have even begun to smell it cooking.

CHILDREN: Mmmm, Mama makes the best soup in all the world!

(All go into the kitchen and sit at the table.)

MARIA: This doesn't look like Mexicali Soup.

ANTONIO: It doesn't smell like Mexicali Soup.

JUAN and MANUEL: It doesn't taste like Mexicali Soup.

ROSITA: This is not Mexicali Soup! This is nothing but hot water!

PAPA: You have forgotten to bring the soup, Mamacita?

MAMA: No, I have not. The soup is in your bowls. And it is just what you wanted. I made the soup the way my family asked me to make it. I left out the potatoes that

Maria does not want. I left out the peppers that Antonio does not want. I left out the onions that Manuel does not want. I left out the tomatoes that Juan does not want. For Rosita I left out the garlic. And for Papa I left out the celery, the little nothing that does not matter. The *new* Mexicali Soup! It is so simple, so quick, so easy to make! You just leave everything out of it!

(All sit still for a minute, then jump up from the table.)

ANTONIO: Mama! If I hurry, I can get to Fernandez's market before it closes. We need a big bunch of hot peppers for your Mexicali Soup.

ROSITA: Good, Antonio! While you are gone, I will get the water boiling and peel the garlic.

MARIA: And I will wash and chop the potatoes.

JUAN and MANUEL: We will get the tomatoes and onions ready—lots of tomatoes and onions!

PAPA: It seems that celery is not such a little nothing after all. *I* will chop the celery. And then we will all enjoy a big bowl of Mama's Mexicali Soup—because Mama makes the best soup in the whole wide world!

Seeing Is Not Believing

RENA MORAN

Did you know that our eyes can play tricks on us? Our eyes can make things appear different from the way they really are. Let's look at some examples of how our eyes can fool us.

Look at the center circles in figures A and B. Which one is larger?

Figure A   Figure B

You probably said that the center circle in figure A is larger than the one in figure B. It's not so! The two center circles are exactly the same size! The center circle in figure A looks larger than it really is because of the small circles around it. The center circle in figure B looks smaller than it really is because of the large circles around it.

Colors can make our eyes play tricks on us. Look at the white jar and the black jar in figure C. Which one is larger?

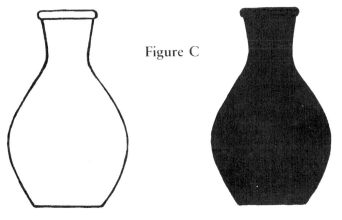

Figure C

Did you say that the white jar is larger than the black jar? If you did, your eyes played a trick on you. Both jars are exactly the same size. The white jar only looks larger than the black one. In general, things that are light colored look larger than things that are dark.

Our eyes can help us to look at the same thing in different ways. Look at figure D. What do you see? Look away, and then look back at the picture again. Do you see something different this time?

Figure D

If you look at this picture one way, you will see the head of a duck. If you look at the picture another way, you will see the head of a rabbit. Which one did you see first?

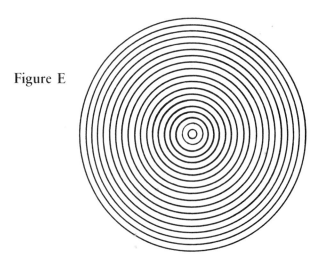

Figure E

Our eyes can also make things seem to move. Count to twenty while you look at the circle in figure E. Do not move your eyes and try not to blink. Does the circle seem to be moving around and around? Of course, it is not really moving at all. Your eyes have fooled you again!

Here is another example of how our eyes can make things appear to move. Look at the tiger standing outside its cage in figure F. Can you think of a way to get it back into its cage?

Figure F

This is how you can get the tiger to go back into its cage. Hold your book in front of your eyes, and look at the empty spot between the tiger and the cage. Slowly move the book toward you until your nose touches the page. Did you see the tiger go into its cage?

Whenever you look at things, keep in mind that your eyes can play tricks on you. Remember to look again, because seeing is not always believing.

The Wolf and the Seven Kids

JACOB and WILHELM GRIMM

[PART 1]

Once upon a time there was a mother goat who had seven little kids that she loved dearly. One day she decided to go into the woods to find tender buds and green leaves for them to eat. She called the kids all together and said, "Whatever you do, watch out for the wolf! Be sure never to let him into the house! If he catches you, he'll eat you up— skin, hair, and all."

Soon after she had gone, the kids heard a knock and "Children dear, open the door. It's your mother."

But the seven little kids called back, "Our mother doesn't have a gruff voice like yours. You're the wolf, and we won't let you in!"

So the wolf ran off to a shop and bought some honey to make his voice soft. Then he knocked on the cottage door and called out, "Open the door, my dears. It's your mother, and I've brought you something nice to eat."

But the wolf's black paw was on the window sill, so the seven little kids shouted back, "Our mother doesn't have black feet. You're the wolf, and we won't let you in!"

Then the wolf went to a baker. "Mr. Baker," he said, "I hurt both my paws this morning. Cover them with some of your fresh dough and sprinkle them with flour." The baker did as the wolf asked.

The wicked wolf rapped on the cottage door for a third time. "Children, dear children," he cried, "it's your mother. I've come home, and I've brought you all kinds of good things to eat."

"Show us your paws!" called out the seven little kids. The wolf put his white paws on the window sill. Then the kids were sure that their mother had really come home, and they ran to open the door. In leaped the wicked wolf!

130

[PART 2]

The kids rushed about in a great panic. One hid under the kitchen table, the second dived under the bed covers, and the third jumped into the oven. The fourth ducked under the kitchen sink, the fifth leaped into the cupboard, and the sixth hid under a chair. Only the smallest kid couldn't find a place to hide. At last he hopped into the tall clock that stood against the wall and pulled the little door shut behind him.

The wolf found them all—but the smallest—and gulped them down. Then, feeling full enough to burst, he went off to the nearest meadow, lay down in the sun, and fell fast asleep.

When the mother goat came home from the wood, what a sight met her eyes! The door was wide open, the table and chairs were overturned, the bed was like a bird's nest, and broken china was all over the floor. She called each of her children by name, but there was no answer until she called the smallest. Then a tiny voice came from the tall clock. "Here I am, Mother!" When the mother goat heard how the wolf had come and eaten all the other children, you can imagine how she wept! The smallest kid, who was still upset, wept along with her.

Finally, the two stopped weeping and went out into the meadow. Just then they caught sight of the wolf, sound asleep beneath a tree and snoring so hard that the branches shook. Something was wriggling around inside him. The mother goat ran to the cottage for scissors and a needle and thread. Quick as a wink, she slit open the wolf's stomach. Out popped one little kid, then another and another, until all six were skipping about on the grass. The wolf was so greedy that he had swallowed them whole.

"Go and fetch me some large stones, and we will put them in the wolf's stomach," the mother goat told her kids. She put all of the stones where the little kids had been. Then she sewed up the wolf's stomach. She was so quick and quiet that the wolf did not even move.

When he woke up, the wolf felt a great weight in his stomach. He said to himself, "Who would think that six little goats would make my stomach rumble so! Oh, how thirsty I am!" He set off for a nearby well to get himself some water. But when he leaned over, the stones were so heavy that he lost his balance, and in he tumbled. So the wicked wolf was drowned.

The seven little kids and their mother danced joyfully around the well, and they lived happily ever after in their little cottage on the edge of the wood.

Clouds

CHRISTINA ROSSETTI

White sheep, white sheep,
On a blue hill,
When the wind stops
You all stand still.
When the wind blows
You walk away slow.
White sheep, white sheep,
Where do you go?

Hot and Cold from One Mouth

AESOP

Once there was a woman who made her living by cutting wood in the forest. One winter day her hands became very cold. She put down her ax and breathed on her hands to warm them. A dwarf who lived in the forest saw this and asked, "Why do you do that?"

"My hands are cold, and I want to warm them with my breath," explained the woodcutter. This answer satisfied the dwarf.

Later in the day the woodcutter built a fire to heat up her noontime meal. She was so hungry, she ate right out of the pot. But, as her soup was still rather hot, she blew on every spoonful to cool it.

This amazed the dwarf, who was still watching her with curiosity. "Why do you blow on the spoon just as you breathed on your cold hands?" he asked.

The woodcutter answered, "I want to cool off my hot soup."

This was too much for the dwarf. "What a strange creature you are!" he cried. "Sometimes your mouth blows hot, and sometimes it blows cold. I'll have nothing more to do with you!" Then he ran away as fast as his legs could carry him.

Hot as an Ice Cube

PHILIP BALESTRINO

Temperature is a measure of how hot or cold something is. An iceberg is cold. It has a low temperature. A fire is hot. It has a high temperature. *Hot* and *cold* are words that describe the temperature of something. So are words like *warm, lukewarm, chilly,* and *freezing.*

When you heat something, its temperature rises. What makes this happen?

Molecules

Everything in the world is made of tiny particles called molecules. Rocks, boats, and ice cream are made of molecules. So are water and milk. You and I are made of molecules too. Things are made of molecules just as a sand castle is made of grains of sand, except that molecules are much, much smaller. They are really too tiny to see or count.

Molecule Movement

Molecules are always moving. They move like popcorn jumping in a popcorn machine. The faster the molecules in something move, the hotter it is. The molecules of a sizzling hot dog move faster than those of a hot dog that has just come from the freezer.

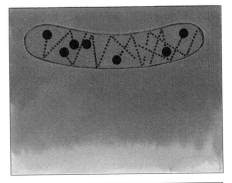

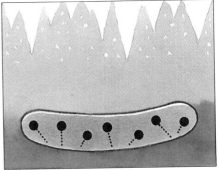

Experiment

You can see that molecules of water move faster when the water is hotter by doing this experiment. Put water in two bowls: cold water in one bowl, hot water in the other. Let the water sit for a minute so that it is very still. Then carefully put a drop of food coloring into the middle of each bowl. In the cold water, the molecules move the food coloring around only a little bit. In the hot water, they move the food coloring around a lot faster.

The more you heat something, the faster its molecules move. This is what causes its temperature to rise.

Moon

WILLIAM JAY SMITH

I have a white cat whose name is Moon;
He eats catfish from a wooden spoon,
And sleeps till five each afternoon.

Moon goes out when the moon is bright
And sycamore trees are spotted white
To sit and stare in the dead of night.

Beyond still water cries a loon,
Through mulberry leaves peers a wild baboon,
And in Moon's eyes I see the moon.

Alex's Bone

HELEN V. GRIFFITH

Alex was digging in the flower bed. "Did you ever bury a bone and then forget where?" he asked the cat.

"Never," said the cat.

"That's amazing," said Alex.

He dug up a marigold. "Oops," he said.

He dug up a petunia. "Oops," he said. "How do you remember where you bury your bones?" he asked the cat.

"Cats don't bury bones," said the cat.

"You just told me that you always find your bones," said Alex.

"I didn't say that," said the cat.

"Are you sure?" asked Alex.

"You should listen better," said the cat.

Alex went back to his digging. "I'd like to find my bone before Robbie comes out to play," he said.

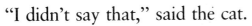

"School started today," said the cat. "Robbie's at school."

"Robbie doesn't need school. He knows everything," said Alex.

"Children go to school for years," said the cat.

"Years!" said Alex. He threw himself on the ground and began to yip. "I want Robbie!" he yipped.

"He'll be back," said the cat.

"But not for years!" yipped Alex.

"Robbie will be home this afternoon," said the cat.

Alex stopped yipping and sat up. "Really?" he asked.

"Of course," said the cat.

"Then why did you tell me that he would be away for years?" asked Alex.

"I didn't say that," said the cat.

"Are you sure?" asked Alex.

"You should listen better," said the cat.

Alex started to dig again. He dug up another petunia. "If I don't find my bone soon," he said, "there won't be any flowers left."

"Eat a biscuit instead," said the cat.

"I'm not hungry," said Alex.

"Then why are you digging up your bone?" asked the cat.

"I'm not digging up my bone," said Alex.

The cat blinked. "You have been talking all morning," he said, "about digging up your bone."

"I'm just looking for it," said Alex.

"Oh," said the cat.

"I'd like to know where it is," said Alex.

"I see," said the cat.

"I don't want to dig it up," said Alex.

"Of course not," said the cat.

"You should listen better," said Alex.

"I should listen less," said the cat.

The Riddle of the Sphinx

A GREEK MYTH

A long, long time ago there lived a monster called the
Sphinx. This Sphinx had the head of a woman, the body of
a lion, and the wings of a bird.

The Sphinx lived near an old city named Thebes.
Whenever a traveler passed by her, she would ask that
person a riddle. If the traveler could not answer the riddle,
the Sphinx would eat the person up.

Here is the riddle of the Sphinx, "What walks on four legs in the morning, on two legs at noon, and on three legs in the evening?"

Many people in Thebes were eaten by the Sphinx because they did not know the answer to this riddle. They were very much afraid of the Sphinx, and they did not know what to do.

Then one day a very clever man came along. His name was Oedipus. As he passed by the Sphinx, she stopped him and asked her riddle, "What walks on four legs in the morning, on two legs at noon, and on three legs in the evening?"

"That is easy," said Oedipus. "The answer is *a human being*, for each of us crawls on all fours as a baby, walks upright when grown, and uses a cane in old age."

This was the right answer. The Sphinx became so angry that she jumped off a cliff and killed herself. Then travelers could pass in safety.

The people of Thebes were so happy and grateful that they made Oedipus their king.

Friday Night Is Papa Night

RUTH A. SONNEBORN

Pedro sat on the kitchen floor, pushing two little cars around and around the legs of his bed.

"Is tonight Friday night, Mama?" he asked.

"Yes," Mama said. "Tonight is Friday night."

Pedro clapped his hands. "Papa is coming. Papa is coming," he sang. "Papa comes every Friday, doesn't he, Mama?"

Mama nodded her head. "Now, Pedro," she said. "Get up on your bed. I have to wash the kitchen floor."

Pedro watched the mop slide back and forth across the kitchen floor. He was glad his bed was in the kitchen where he could watch Mama work.

"Mama," he said, "why doesn't Papa come home every night? Ana's papa comes home every night. Why not my papa?"

Mama sighed. "Poor Papa," she said, "has to work very hard. He has to have two jobs to get enough money so we can eat and have a place to live. His jobs are far from here, too."

"When I get big," Pedro said, "I'll help Papa. I'll take one of his jobs. Then Papa can come home every night."

"Yes," Mama said. "Some day Papa will come home every night. It will happen, Pedro. It will happen."

The door opened, and Manuela, Carlos, and Ricardo came in together from school.

"Tonight is Friday night," Pedro shouted. "Papa is coming."

"Who doesn't know that, silly?" Carlos said.

"Never mind the talk," Mama said. "We have work to do. Everyone gets a job.

"You, Manuela, you wash and pick over the beans." Mama pointed to the sink.

"You, Carlos, run to the store. I forgot to buy onions." She handed Carlos her purse.

"And you, Ricardo, take the trash downstairs, please, and dump it."

"What about me?" Pedro asked. "Don't I get a job?"

"Sure," Mama said. "You get a job, too. Here, help your brother. Take this small basket of trash down."

By late afternoon the jobs were done. The table was set. The kitchen was filled with smells that made everyone hungry.

Pedro went to the window. He stared down into the street. It was beginning to grow dark.

"I don't see Papa," he said.

Manuela looked at the kitchen clock. "He's awfully late already, Mama," she said. "What could have happened?"

"Don't worry," Mama said. "Papa will come."

They waited and waited.

Finally, Mama went to the stove.

"Come, *niños*," she said. "We must eat. Papa will come while we eat."

The children came to the table. No one talked.

Then Pedro said, "I don't want any supper. I want Papa." He began to cry. He got up from the table and crawled onto his bed. Mama came over. She covered him with a blanket.

"O.K., Pedro," she said. "Go to sleep now."

Pedro sat up. "No, no, no," he shouted. "I don't want to sleep. I want to wait for Papa."

Mama hugged him. "Go to sleep now, Pedro," she said. "I will wake you when Papa comes."

"Sure?" Pedro asked. "Promise?"

"Promise," Mama said.

Pedro's eyes closed.

Suddenly Pedro awoke. He opened his eyes. The kitchen was very dark and empty. There was just one spot of light on the floor by the window.

Pedro sat up in bed. And then he remembered. Papa. Papa had not come home.

Pedro got out of bed and ran to the window. He looked down into the street. There was no one there. Then a cat ran across the street. A policeman walked slowly past.

He saw a dark shadow moving. The shadow moved closer. Was it? Yes, it was a man. It was a man carrying a fat shopping bag. Papa always brought a fat shopping bag home with him. The man came closer. Papa! Pedro was sure it was Papa.

He hurried across the kitchen and turned on the light. The kitchen now looked brighter than day. He ran to the door and opened it wide.

"Papa," Pedro shouted. "Papa, you're here." He hugged Papa and Papa hugged him.

In another minute Mama, Manuela, Ricardo, and Carlos came running from their beds. "Papa, Papa, what happened?" everyone asked at the same time.

"My friend Juan who works with me got sick," Papa said. "I took him to the hospital. Then I went to tell his wife."

Mama took Papa by the hand. "Come, sit down. You must be very tired."

Papa sat down. "You know," he said, "coming home now I was so tired. So very tired. I thought, everyone will be sleeping. No one will be at the door to meet me. But suddenly there was a light in the kitchen window. Someone was up. Someone was waiting. And"—he pulled Pedro onto his lap—"it was my Pedro. My Pedro was at the door waiting for me. And suddenly I was not tired any more."

Papa hugged Pedro and set him down on the floor. He drew the fat shopping bag toward him.

"Come now," he said. "Let's begin." He dipped his hand into the bag.

He handed out sneakers for Pedro, a blouse for Manuela, socks for Carlos, and pajamas for Ricardo. To Mama he gave one red rose.

"It's just like Christmas when Papa comes home," Pedro said. "Just like Christmas."

Mama heaped Papa's plate with fish and beans, and everyone sat around the table talking, laughing, watching Papa eat.

"Yes," Pedro said dreamily, "Friday night is the nicest night. Friday night is Papa night."

Unit Five
Surprises

A Parakeet Named Dreidel

ISAAC B. SINGER

It happened on Chanukkah about ten years ago. All day
long a heavy snow was falling. Towards evening the sky
cleared and a few stars appeared. A frost set in. The snow
on the street sparkled like diamonds. It was the eighth day
of Chanukkah, and my silver Chanukkah lamp stood on the
window sill with all nine candles burning. It was mirrored in
the windowpane, and I imagined another lamp outside.

My wife Esther was frying potato pancakes, which are
a Chanukkah treat. I sat with my son David at a table and
played dreidel with him. Suddenly David cried out, "Papa,
look!" And he pointed to the window.

I looked up. I could hardly believe what I saw! Outside
on the window sill stood a yellow-green bird watching the
Chanukkah candles. In a moment I understood what had
happened. A parakeet had escaped from its home. It had
flown out into the cold street and had landed on my
window sill, perhaps attracted by the light.

A parakeet comes from warmer countries. It cannot
stand the cold and frost for very long. At once I set out to

save the bird from freezing. First I carried away the
Chanukkah lamp so that the bird should not burn itself
when it came in. Then I opened the window and with a
quick wave of my hand shooed the parakeet inside. The
whole thing took only a few seconds.

In the beginning the frightened bird flew from wall to
wall. It hit itself against the ceiling. David tried to calm it.
"Don't be afraid, little bird, we are your friends." Presently
the bird flew towards David and landed on his head, as
though it had been trained and was used to people. David

153

began to dance and laugh from joy. My wife in the kitchen heard the noise and came out to see what had happened. When she saw the bird on David's head, she asked, "Where did you get a bird all of a sudden?"

"Mama, it just came to our window."

"To the window in the middle of winter?"

"Papa saved its life. It's a Chanukkah miracle!"

Soon the bird was not afraid of us. David lifted his hand to his forehead, and the bird settled on his finger. Esther placed a saucer of millet and a dish with water on the table, and the parakeet ate and drank. Then it saw the dreidel and began to push it with its beak. David exclaimed, "Look, the bird plays dreidel."

David soon began to talk about buying a cage for the bird and also about giving it a name. Esther and I reminded him that the bird was not ours. We would try to find the owners, who probably missed the parakeet and worried about what had happened to it in the icy weather. David said, "Meanwhile, let's call it Dreidel."

That night Dreidel slept on a picture frame. In the morning it woke us with its singing and talking in Yiddish. We were filled with wonder and delight to hear a tiny parakeet talk!

The next day I posted a notice in the elevators of the

neighborhood houses. It said that we had found a Yiddish-speaking parakeet. When a few days passed and no one called, I advertised in the newspaper for which I wrote. A week went by and no one claimed the bird. Only then did Dreidel become ours. We bought a large cage with all the toys that a bird might want. Because Chanukkah is a festival of freedom, we decided never to lock the cage. Dreidel was free to fly around the house whenever *he* pleased. (The man at the pet shop had told us that the bird was male.)

Dreidel is still with us, always eager to learn new words and new games. On Chanukkah he always gets a gift—a mirror, a ladder, a bathtub, a swing, or a jingle-bell. He even likes potato pancakes, as a parakeet named Dreidel should.

Where's Willie?

EVE BUNTING

We have a chameleon named Willie.

My mom, my sister Keke, and I like Willie a lot. It's fun to play hide-and-seek with him. Willie hides and we seek. Willie changes his color to match what he's lying on. When he's on our green couch, Willie's green. When he's on our brown rug, Willie's brown.

Dad doesn't like Willie at all. That's because once he almost *lay* on him when Willie got into Dad's bed. Yellow sheets and yellow Willie.

"Keep that lousy lizard out of my bed," Dad yelled.

"He's not a lizard, he's a chameleon," Mom said.

"He's a pest," Dad told her.

Dad's an artist, and he's always careful to keep his studio door closed—because of Willie.

One evening Dad was bringing home a customer whose name was Mr. Rich. Mr. Rich had built a bunch of houses outside of town, and he wanted Dad to do an advertisement for him.

Mom had made mandarin tea and her yummy Pagoda Friendship cake to sweeten up Mr. Rich, and Keke and I had tidied the house and ourselves. We were all ready when Keke suddenly said, "Where's Willie?"

Mom went *"Hssss"* and rolled her eyes. "Where *is* Willie?"

We looked in all of Willie's favorite places but with no luck. "Oh, dear," Mom said. "Here's Dad. Not a word about Willie," she warned. "But seek, girls, seek."

Mom, Dad, and Mr. Rich sat at the kitchen table and had mandarin tea and Pagoda Friendship cake. Before they sat down, Keke and I ran our hands all over their chairs, seeking Willie. Safe! When Mr. Rich stood and said, "Well now, how about a look at your poster, Jim," Keke and I scampered ahead of him on the stairs, seeking on each step.

"Lively little girls you have there," Mr. Rich said. He looked a little taken aback. Since we're half Chinese, he probably thought sweeping the stairs in front of guests was some ancient Chinese custom.

"Uh-oh," Keke said as she looked at Dad's studio door. It was open, and it was my fault because I tidied the studio.

"Well," Dad said. "Would you like to come over to my drawing table, Mr. Rich?"

Mr. Rich ambled across the room.

Keke and I walked in front of him, seeking desperately.

Dad's oversized watercolor was spread on his big table.

Keke went *"Hsss!"* and put her hands over her mouth. Keke gets her hsssing from Mother. I looked at the poster and wanted to hsss myself.

"I think this says what needs to be said about your new development," Dad said.

Underneath the slogan were the red-roofed houses, the blue lake, the green golf course—and a chameleon spread out by the first green.

"He's asleep," I whispered to Keke.

"Clever! Clever!" Mr. Rich said, and Dad looked bewildered because, let's face it, he hadn't done anything clever. The painting was pretty, sure. But the words were kind of dumb.

"I like it, I like it," Mr. Rich said. "A nice touch, that—putting in the kind of lizard that changes color."

"He's a chameleon," I said.

Dad jerked his head round at Willie and then at us. *"Hsss!"* he said. He's picked up Mom's hsssing, too. Then Dad realized that Mr. Rich was smiling and rubbing his hands together.

"You'll blend right in! A little humor there. Humor sells houses," Mr. Rich boomed. He leaned forward, one arm outstretched.

"Don't touch," Dad said quickly. "It's . . . it's . . ."

"It's still soft," I said. I'm good at not lying.

"Well, I'm sold, I'm sold." Mr. Rich was turning away. "Come to my office tomorrow, Jim, and we'll sign on the deal."

As soon as he and Dad disappeared, I picked up Willie. He immediately turned yellow, which he does when he's mad. Willie hates to be disturbed.

So Dad sold his art, and now the posters with their fake chameleons are all over town: *Chameleon Homes. You'll blend right in.*

You'd think Dad would like Willie now after what Willie did for him. Dad doesn't say. But every time he goes out he brings home mealworms for Willie, which is nice, because mealworms are Willie's favorite thing in the whole world. But Willie won't eat them if Dad's looking. Willie is very independent.

An Emerald Is as Green as Grass

CHRISTINA ROSSETTI

An emerald is as green as grass,
  A ruby red as blood.
A sapphire shines as blue as heaven;
  A flint lies in the mud.

A diamond is a brilliant stone,
  To catch the world's desire.
An opal holds a fiery spark;
  But a flint holds fire.

The Tale of Peter Rabbit

BEATRIX POTTER

[PART 1]

Once upon a time there were four little
Rabbits, and their names were Flopsy, Mopsy,
Cotton-tail, and Peter.

They lived with their mother in a
sandbank, underneath the root of a very big
fir tree.

"Now, my dears," said old Mrs. Rabbit
one morning, "you may go into the fields or
down the lane, but don't go into Mr.
McGregor's garden. Your father had an
accident there; he was put into a pie by Mrs.
McGregor. Now run along, and don't get into
mischief. I am going out."

Then old Mrs. Rabbit took a basket and
her umbrella and went through the wood to
the baker's. She bought a loaf of brown bread
and five currant buns.

Flopsy, Mopsy, and Cotton-tail, who
were good little bunnies, went down the lane
to gather blackberries; but Peter, who was
very naughty, ran straight away to Mr.
McGregor's garden and squeezed under
the gate!

First he ate some lettuce and some French
beans; and then he ate some radishes; and
then, feeling rather sick, he went to look for
some parsley.

But around the end of a cucumber frame,
whom should he meet but Mr. McGregor!

Mr. McGregor was on his hands and
knees planting young cabbages, but he jumped
up and ran after Peter, waving a rake and
calling out, "Stop, thief!"

Peter was most dreadfully frightened; he
rushed all over the garden, for he had
forgotten the way back to the gate.

· He lost one of his shoes among the
cabbages and the other shoe among the
potatoes.

After losing them, he ran on four legs
and went faster, so I think he might have got

away altogether if he had not unfortunately run into a gooseberry net and got caught by the large buttons on his jacket. It was a blue jacket with brass buttons, quite new.

Peter gave himself up for lost and shed big tears, but his sobs were overheard by some friendly sparrows, who flew to him in great excitement and implored him to exert himself.

Mr. McGregor came up with a sieve, which he intended to pop upon the top of Peter; but Peter wriggled out just in time, leaving his jacket behind him, rushed into the toolshed, and jumped into a can. It would have been a beautiful thing to hide in if it had not had so much water in it.

Mr. McGregor was quite sure that Peter was somewhere in the toolshed, perhaps hidden underneath a flowerpot. He began to turn them over carefully, looking under each.

Presently Peter sneezed—"Kerty-schoo!" Mr. McGregor was after him in no time and tried to put his foot upon Peter, who jumped out of a window, upsetting three plants. The window was too small for Mr. McGregor, and he was tired of running after Peter. He went back to his work.

[PART 2]

Peter sat down to rest; he was out of breath and trembling with fright, and he had not the least idea which way to go. Also he was very damp with sitting in that can.

After a time Peter began to wander about, going lippity—lippity—not very fast, and looking all around.

He found a door in a wall; but it was locked, and there was no room for a fat little rabbit to squeeze underneath.

An old mouse was running in and out over the stone doorstep, carrying peas and beans to her family in the wood. Peter asked her the way to the gate, but she had such a large pea in her mouth that she could not answer. She only shook her head at him. Peter began to cry.

Then he tried to find his way straight

across the garden, but he became more and more puzzled. Presently he came to a pond where Mr. McGregor filled his water cans. A white cat was staring at some goldfish; she sat very, very still, but now and then the tip of her tail twitched as if it were alive. Peter thought it best to go away without speaking to her; he had heard about cats from his cousin, little Benjamin Bunny.

He went back toward the toolshed, but suddenly, quite close to him, he heard the noise of a hoe—scr-r-ritch, scratch, scratch, scritch. Peter scuttered underneath the bushes. But presently, as nothing happened, he came out, and climbed upon a wheelbarrow, and peeped over. The first thing he saw was Mr. McGregor hoeing onions. His back was turned toward Peter, and beyond him was the gate!

Peter got down very quietly off the wheelbarrow and started running as fast as he could go, along a straight walk behind some black-currant bushes.

Mr. McGregor caught sight of him at the

corner, but Peter did not care. He slipped
under the gate, and was safe at last in the
wood outside the garden.

Mr. McGregor hung up the little jacket
and the shoes for a scarecrow to frighten the
blackbirds. Peter never stopped running or
looked behind him till he got home to the big
fir tree.

He was so tired that he flopped down
upon the nice soft sand on the floor of the
rabbit hole and shut his eyes. His mother was
busy cooking; she wondered what he had
done with his clothes. It was the second little
jacket and pair of shoes that Peter had lost in
a fortnight!

I am sorry to say that Peter was not very
well during the evening. His mother put him
to bed and made some camomile tea; and she
gave a dose of it to Peter!

"One tablespoonful to be taken at bedtime."

But Flopsy, Mopsy, and Cotton-tail had
bread and milk and blackberries for supper.

Androcles and the Lion

A ROMAN TALE

Androcles was a brave soldier and one of the emperor's favorites. Once, though, he displeased the emperor by shooting a deer that the emperor had missed. He was sold to be a slave and sent to a faraway land. One day, many years later, when he could bear the life of a slave no longer, Androcles ran away.

When he could run no farther, Androcles stopped running and went into a cave cut into the side of a hill. He was weak from heat and hunger, and it was cool and dark in the cave. Androcles was glad to rest.

Then he heard something that made his heart stand still. Soft feet were padding toward him, and there was a strong, wild, animal smell in the cave. Androcles froze and looked toward the opening of the cave.

In came a great, golden lion limping badly. There was a huge thorn in his right front paw. The lion saw Androcles, but he was in too much pain to care. He flopped down on one side, moaning gently.

Although Androcles was very much afraid, he was also

a very kind man. He couldn't bear the lion's moaning. He inched closer to the beast. Then, as fast as a snake, he reached over and yanked out the thorn!

With a grumbling purr, the lion began licking his poor, hurt paw. From time to time he licked Androcles as well. At last, worn out by the day's troubles, the two fell asleep.

Androcles and the lion became friends. They stayed together in the little cave for many days. Then one morning, when Androcles was gathering berries for breakfast, he ran right into a band of Roman soldiers! The soldiers knew at once that Androcles was a runaway slave. They tied him up and took him back to Rome.

Now, in ancient Roman times runaway slaves often suffered cruel punishments, and this is what happened to Androcles. He was shut up in a small, dark room that opened onto a large arena. There, in ten days' time, he would be thrown to a hungry lion. The emperor disliked Androcles even more now, because he had run away from his master. The emperor and many other Romans would make a game of watching the lion eat poor Androcles.

At last the dreaded day came. People poured into the arena, laughing and talking and wearing their brightest clothes. It was like a giant party—for everyone except Androcles.

Then, from the royal seat, the emperor raised his hand. The door of Androcles' little room swung open. Soldiers pushed him out into the middle of the arena.

The emperor raised his hand again. Another door opened, and this time an enormous lion sprang into the arena. He let out a mighty roar, his tail swishing angrily to and fro.

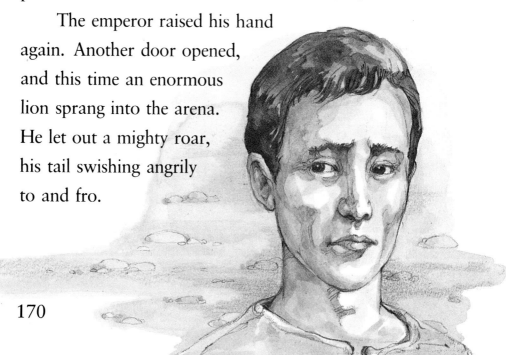

"This is the end," thought Androcles, bravely turning to face the lion. But what was this? A rough, friendly tongue slid across his face, and the lion gave a deep purr. It was the same lion that Androcles had helped in the cave.

It was amazing, and the people loved it! "Free him!" they shouted wildly. "Free the slave!"

Even the emperor was impressed. He raised his hand a third time, and the gates to the arena were opened wide. Then, turning their backs on the emperor and crowd and city, Androcles and the lion walked off together toward freedom.

Fidelia

RUTH ADAMS

[PART 1]

Fidelia Ortega belonged to a musical family. Her father played the trumpet with a band. Her brother Alberto and her sister Carmela were in the school orchestra. Alberto played the trombone, Carmela the clarinet.

Fidelia wanted to play in the school orchestra, too. She wanted to play a violin. But she was only in second grade, and the youngest children in the orchestra were fourth-graders.

When Ms. Toomey found out how badly Fidelia wanted to be in the orchestra, she let her play the tom-tom for the Indian dance. It was fun, and Fidelia did her best, but it wasn't the same as singing out the melody on a beautiful violin.

One day Ms. Toomey announced that some players from their school would be chosen for the All City Orchestra. Ms. Reed, the head music teacher, was coming the next week to hear them play. Fidelia wanted to play for Ms. Reed. If only she had a violin!

172

Then Fidelia had an idea. She would make a violin. She started with a cigar box and some scrap lumber. Alberto and Carmela helped her, and with blocks of wood, rubber bands, some nails, and a clothespin they made a violin. It sounded pretty good for a make-believe violin.

Fidelia practiced and practiced on her cigar-box violin. Finally she knew exactly how to make the sounds she wanted.

The day came for Ms. Reed to choose the players for the All City Orchestra. Fidelia let Carmela and Alberto start to school ahead of her. As soon as they were out of sight, she wrapped her violin in a piece of old sheet and put it in a grocery bag.

She scooted down the street. I mustn't be late, she thought.

The orchestra was tuning up when Fidelia tiptoed through the door. Her heart began to *thump, thump.*

"Hurry up! We are going to play the Indian dance first. Ms. Reed is already here," Carmela whispered.

Fidelia propped her grocery bag in the corner and got the tom-tom.

She watched Ms. Toomey. She counted carefully. She played her very best. And all the while she thought her heart must sound louder than the tom-tom.

After the Indian dance Ms. Reed clapped and said, "I see we are going to find many players here for the All City Orchestra."

Ms. Toomey said, "Next, we will play 'Lullaby.'"

That was what Fidelia had been waiting for. Quietly, she unwrapped the cigar-box violin. With loving care, she tucked it under her jaw.

The silvery little melody of the solo violins slipped around the room like moonlight. Fidelia knew just where to place her fingers to match the notes.

[PART 2]

Bzzz . . . bzzz . . . zubb . . . zubb . . . !
Ms. Toomey tapped her baton on her music stand.

Bzzz . . . bz . . . Suddenly Fidelia saw that everyone else had stopped playing. They were all looking at her.

"Oh no," wailed Carmela.

"Not here!" moaned Alberto.

Fidelia felt hot all over.

"Fidelia, come up here," said Ms. Toomey.

Fidelia came.

"What is this?" asked Ms. Toomey.

"I made it. Alberto and Carmela helped me."

Ms. Reed held out her hand. "May I see it?" she asked.
She examined the cigar-box violin. "Was this your own
idea?" she asked.

Fidelia nodded.

"It was a good idea, but I'm afraid that you cannot play a tune on this violin—only pretend music."

"Oh, but I can play a tune," cried Fidelia. "I practiced. May I show you?"

Ms. Reed smiled and nodded.

Fidelia carefully tucked the cigar box under her jaw. She began to pluck away at the rubber bands.

Sure enough, a good listener could hear the tune of "The Farmer in the Dell" among the twanging, buzzing rubber-band noises.

Ms. Reed was a good listener. She watched closely, too. "Where did you learn the correct position for playing a violin?" she asked when Fidelia had finished.

"I watched the others. I did what I heard Ms. Toomey tell them to do."

"Would you like to play a real violin?"

"Oh, yes!" said Fidelia.

"Hm," said Ms. Reed. She took Ms. Toomey aside and spoke to her softly. Ms. Toomey smiled and called to Alberto. Ms. Reed handed Alberto her car keys and whispered in his ear. Alberto ran out the door. In two minutes he was back. Under his arm was a violin case.

Ms. Reed opened the case. "Let's see how this violin fits, Fidelia."

It fit Fidelia exactly right. She knew by the way the smooth, black chin rest cradled the corner of her jaw.

She knew by the way her elbow crooked neatly under the shining body of the violin exactly where it should. She knew by the feel of the neck resting on her thumb . . . not too light, not too heavy. She knew by the way her fingers curled over the fingerboard.

"Fidelia," said Ms. Reed, "I am going to leave this violin here for you to use. Ms. Toomey will start you in beginning string class. I will come back in a month to see how you are getting along. If you are doing well, we will make a regular instrument loan for you. How does that sound?"

"Wonderful!" breathed Fidelia. "Will I be able to play in the All City Orchestra?"

Ms. Reed laughed. "Not this time," she said, "but if you do as well as I think you will, I'm sure you will be in it next year."

The musical family of Fidelia Ortega was well represented in the All City Orchestra.

Toom-room-room-room!

That was Alberto's trombone.

Tootle-tee, tootle-tee, tootle-tum-tee!

That was Carmela's clarinet.

This year it was Fidelia's turn to sit in the audience and clap, but she didn't care. She had a violin, and she was in the beginning string class.

Everybody has to start somewhere.

The Sleeping Beauty

JACOB and WILHELM GRIMM

[PART 1]

A long time ago there lived a king and queen who wanted a child more than anything in the world. When at long last their wish was granted and a little girl was born to them, they were overjoyed.

To celebrate, the proud king gave a great feast. He invited all of his relatives and friends, and almost all the fairies in the land. There were thirteen fairies in the kingdom; but as the king had only twelve golden plates, one fairy had to be left at home.

When the feast was at an end, each of the fairies offered a gift to the little princess.

"You shall be the fairest of all," said the first fairy.

"You shall be loved by everyone for your good heart and your kindness," said the next.

"And you will be clever as well as good," said a third.

"You shall sing like a nightingale," said another.

By the time eleven of the fairies had given their gifts, the princess had everything the heart could hope for. At that very moment the door to the great hall banged open and in marched the thirteenth fairy. She was in a fury!

"You did not ask me to come," she cried, "so in return I tell you that when the princess is fifteen years old, she will prick her finger on a spindle and fall down dead!" And without another word the fairy turned and was gone.

Everyone was terrified, and there was a great confusion. But then the twelfth fairy stepped forward. "Don't despair," she said. "I cannot undo the curse, but I can soften it. The princess will not die. She will fall into a deep sleep for a hundred years."

To try to save his child, the king ordered that every spindle in the kingdom should be burned.

As the years went by, it seemed that all would be well. The fairy wishes all came true. The princess grew up so beautiful and kind and clever that everyone who knew her loved her dearly.

But on the day she was fifteen years old, she took it into her head to explore every corner of the castle. She wandered from room to room until at last she found herself in a part of the castle she had never seen before. She climbed a winding stair into a dusty old tower. There was a little door with a rusty key in it. When she turned the key, the door flew open. There in the tiny room sat an old woman with a spindle, busily spinning her flax.

Now as you know, the princess had never seen a spindle in her life. So she said, "Good day to you, old woman.

What in the world are you doing?"

"I am spinning," the old woman answered, nodding her head.

"What is that thing that bobs about so?" asked the princess. "Do let me try!" But no sooner did she pick up the spindle than the bad wish came true, and she pricked her finger. At once she fell into a deep sleep.

[PART 2]

A great quiet spread over the whole castle. The king and queen fell asleep upon their thrones with their courtiers about them. The horses slept in the stable, the dogs in the yard, the doves on the roof, and the flies on the walls. Even the fire on the hearth died down and slept. The roast stopped spitting, and the cook (who was pulling the kitchen boy's ear) began to snore. The wind dropped, and not a leaf stirred in the big trees.

Around the castle a hedge of thorns sprang up. It grew higher and thicker with every year that passed. After many years, the castle—even the flag on the tower—could not be seen at all. Far and wide people told stories of the Sleeping Beauty. Many a prince came to free her; but the thorns were like claws, and not one prince could force his way through.

Long years went by, and one day a king's son came riding through the land. He heard the tales of the castle beyond the hedge and of the beautiful sleeping princess. He also heard of the many kings' sons who had tried—and failed—to free the princess. But this did not discourage him. "I will go in and see this lovely princess," he said.

By this time the hundred years had passed. It was time for Sleeping Beauty to wake again. When the prince stepped up to the hedge, each thorn became a flower, and the hedge parted to let him through. In the castle yard he saw the

horses sleeping on their feet, the dogs asleep in the sun, and the doves on the roof with their heads tucked under their wings.

He saw the flies sleeping on the walls, the fire asleep on the hearth, and the cook still snoring with her hand on the kitchen boy's ear. And in the great hall he saw the king and queen sound asleep among their lords and ladies.

At last he climbed to the tower. There lay the princess, still fast asleep. She was so beautiful that he could not take his eyes off her. He bent down and kissed her.

At the touch of his lips the magic spell was broken. Sleeping Beauty opened her eyes and smiled up at the prince.

The prince and Sleeping Beauty went down from the tower hand in hand. Then the king and queen and all their court woke up and looked about with wide eyes. The horses shook themselves and stamped. The dogs jumped up and wagged their tails. The doves ruffled their feathers and flew down to peck the grain. The flies on the wall began to crawl. The fire flared up, the roast sizzled, the cook pulled the kitchen boy's ear, and the kitchen boy howled.

Then Sleeping Beauty and her prince were married in great splendor, and they lived happily ever after.

Brothers: A Hebrew Legend

Retold by FLORENCE B. FREEDMAN

Long, long ago in the land of Israel, there lived a farmer named Seth. Seth had two sons, Dan and Joel.

Every spring and every fall Seth plowed the earth. From the time they were little boys, Dan and Joel followed him, planting the seeds. Then they watched the wheat grow from tiny plants to tall stalks.

When the wheat was ripe, Seth took his sickle and cut it down. The boys helped him tie it in bundles and load it onto their donkey. Then they rode to the threshing floor and piled the wheat high.

Dan and Joel grew and grew until they were taller than the plow, taller than the wheat . . . taller than their father.

When Seth grew old, he called his sons to him. "You are good men and good farmers," he said. "You are good sons to me and to your mother. I am too old to plow and plant and stack and thresh the wheat. I will soon die.

"When I do, I will divide my land in half. You, Dan, will get one part, and you, Joel, the other. I know that you will always be friends and help each other."

After their father died, Dan and Joel divided the land. Each built a house.

Joel married a lovely woman named Miriam. Miriam and Joel had three sons. Joel's sons helped their father, just as Dan and Joel had helped their father.

Dan did not marry. He lived alone in his little house. He went to visit Joel and his family whenever he could.

When Joel's boys were twelve and ten and three years old, there came a bad year. The rains did not fall. The wheat dried up. There were not many bundles of wheat on the threshing floor.

One night Joel could not sleep.

"What is the matter?" asked Miriam.

"I am thinking about my brother," Joel answered. "He is all alone. You and I have sons to take care of us when we are old. Dan has nobody. Yet we have the same amount of land and the same amount of wheat. It isn't fair."

"What will you do about it?" asked Miriam.

"I will take some of our wheat to my brother," answered Joel.

Joel dressed quickly and left the house. He shook his sleepy donkey. "Wake up! We have work to do!" he said. In the quiet of the dark night he took wheat to his brother's threshing floor and silently went home.

On the same night Dan could not sleep. He was thinking about his brother. My brother Joel has a wife and three children. He has five people to feed and I have only myself. Yet he has the same amount of land. It isn't fair, he thought.

Quietly he got out of bed, loaded his donkey with wheat, and took it to his brother's threshing floor.

In the morning Joel looked at his wheat. He rubbed his eyes. "Can it be?" he said to himself. "There is just as much wheat here today as there was yesterday. I must take more to Dan tonight."

In the morning Dan, too, looked at his wheat. He rubbed his eyes. I did not take my brother as much wheat as I meant to, he thought.

Joel told his family what had happened.

"Tonight we will help you," said Miriam and the boys.

That night Joel awakened Miriam and the boys. "It is time," he said. They loaded the donkey, and Joel, Miriam and the boys carried as much wheat as they could.

That night Dan started out with his load of wheat at the same time as Joel.

They met halfway, at the place where their farms joined. Without saying a word, they dropped their bundles of wheat and hugged each other.

Then they heard a soft voice that came from everywhere and nowhere singing, "How good it is for brothers to live together in friendship."

Hundreds of years passed. A city grew where Seth's farm had been—the city of Jerusalem. And King Solomon built the Holy Temple on the spot where the brothers had met and hugged each other.

When the Temple was finished, a soft, low voice was heard singing, "How good it is for brothers to live together in friendship."

The song came from nowhere—and everywhere.

Seymour the Prince

SUE ALEXANDER

Seymour's friends in the Maple Street Club are putting on a play in Cindy's garage. The play is *Sleeping Beauty*, and his friends want Seymour to play the Prince. Seymour is afraid that everyone will laugh when the Prince kisses Sleeping Beauty, and he decides to have nothing to do with the play. His friends say they'll find another Prince. But as show time draws closer, Seymour can't help being curious.

It was Saturday. When Seymour came outside he saw the sign on Cindy's garage. The side door was open. Seymour peeked inside.

PLAY STARTS AT 2:00pm 5¢

190

The two chairs looked like thrones. The big piece of cardboard had a spining wheel painted on it. Melissa's wings were against the wall. Cindy's baby doll was on the floor. And the sheet made a perfect curtain.

Just then the Maple Street Club came into the garage.

"We thought we saw you," Stacey said.

"I—I—wanted to see if you were ready," Seymour said.

"We're *almost* ready," Cindy said. "We just have to rehearse one more time."

"Oh," Seymour said. And he started to leave.

"You don't have to go," Butch said. "In fact, you can help."

"How?" Seymour asked.

"Well," Cindy said, "if you stand where the Prince is supposed to stand, we can see how everything looks."

"Where's the Prince?" Seymour asked.

"He'll be here soon," Butch said. "But we need to rehearse *now*."

"Oh, all right," Seymour said. "I guess I can help for a while."

"Here's the Prince costume," Melissa said.

"I thought this was just a rehearsal," Seymour said.

"It is," Cindy said. "It's a *dress* rehearsal."

"Oh," Seymour said. And he put on the jacket and the hat.

"All right," Cindy said. "Let's begin."

Seymour stood where Andy told him to. He watched Melissa be the Bad Fairy. He watched Cindy prick her finger. He watched them all go into the Enchanted Sleep.

"Now the Prince is supposed to kiss Sleeping Beauty," Andy said.

"Oh, no!" Seymour said. "Not even in the rehearsal!"

192

Just then people started coming in. Seymour and Cindy
looked out through the hole in the sheet. The River Street
Club was there. Butch's little brother was there. So was
Andy's little sister. Cindy's big sister was there with two of
her friends. And some other big kids were there.

"It's time for *me* to get out of here," Seymour said.

"Take *one* step out of here, Seymour, and you're out of
the Maple Street Club FOREVER!" Cindy said. And she
stamped her foot—hard.

Seymour looked at Cindy. She didn't look at him. Then
Seymour said, "You never *got* anyone else to be the Prince,
did you!"

"No," Cindy said.

"But I told you I wouldn't *kiss* anyone!" Seymour said.

"We hoped you'd change your mind," Butch said.

Seymour looked at the Maple Street Club. They were all looking at him. He looked through the hole in the sheet again. He looked at all the big kids. He thought about kissing Cindy. He thought about everyone's laughing.

"I'm not going to kiss ANYONE!" Seymour said. "Call off the play! I'm going home!"

"But I've got my wings on!" Melissa wailed.

Just then Andy went to the audience side of the sheet. "Ladies and gentlemen!" he said in his introducer voice. "The Maple Street Club will now act *Sleeping Beauty*!"

Everybody clapped. Butch pulled the sheet back. And the play began.

Everybody said, "Boo!" when Melissa put the curse on Cindy's baby doll. Everybody yelled, "Watch out!" when Cindy got near the spinning wheel. Everybody laughed when Stacey said, "Ow," as she fell into the Enchanted Sleep.

Then it was time for the Prince to come. Seymour could feel everyone waiting.

He thought about *kissing* Cindy. He thought about everyone's laughing. He thought about the Maple Street Club. He thought very hard. Then he sighed. Seymour closed his eyes. He took a deep breath. And he came out from behind the sheet.

"HOORAY!" yelled one of the big kids. "The Prince will save Sleeping Beauty!"

"HOORAY!" everybody yelled.

Seymour stopped. He opened his eyes. Everybody was clapping!

Seymour stood up very straight. Then he went over to Cindy. Everybody was very quiet.

"What's this?" Seymour said. "A beautiful Princess! And she's fast asleep."

And Seymour bent over and kissed Sleeping Beauty.

"HOORAY!" everybody yelled. "HOORAY for the Prince! He saved Sleeping Beauty!" They clapped and whistled and cheered.

Seymour looked around. "I did it!" he thought. "I kissed Sleeping Beauty and NOBODY laughed!" And he smiled.

Then Seymour, the Prince, bowed—and bowed again. And everyone said the Maple Street Club put on very good plays.

Glossary

Pronunciation Key

a_, ă_	apple, tan	g	gas, wiggle, sag
ā	acorn, table	ġ	gem, giant, gym
à	alone, Donna	gh_	ghost
â	air, care	_gh	though, thought (silent)
ä	father, wand	h_	hat
ạ	all, ball	i_, ĭ_	it, sit
a_e	ape, bake	ī	pilot, pie
ai_	aim, sail	_ï_	babies, machine, *also*
àr	calendar		onion, savior, familiar
är	art, park, car	i_e	ice, bite
au_	author, Paul	_igh	high, bright
aw	awful, lawn, saw	ir	irk, bird, fir
_ay	say, day	j_	jam
b	bat, able, tub	k	kite, ankle, ink
c	cat, cot, cut	kn_	knife
ce	cent, ace	l	lamp, wallet, tail
ch	chest, church	_le	table, ample
c̄h	chorus, ache	m	man, bump, ham
c̆h	chute	_mb	lamb, comb
ci	cider, decide	n	no, tent, sun
_c̱i_	special	_n̄_	uncle, anger
_ck	tack, sick	_ng	sing, ring
cy	bicycle	o_, ŏ_	odd, pot
d	dad	ō	go, no, toe
_dge	edge, judge	ȯ	come, wagon
e_, ĕ_	elf, hen	ô	off, song
ē	equal, me	oa_	oat, soap
ė	moment, loaded	o_e	ode, bone
ea	eat, leap, tea	oi_	oil, boil
_ĕa_	head, bread	o͝o	book, nook
ee	eel, feet, see	o͞o	boot, zoo
er	herd, her	or	order, normal
_ew	few, blew	ȯr	motor, doctor
f	far, taffy, off	ou_	out, hound

198

ow	owl, town, cow	ụ̄	truth, true
_ōw	low, throw	ů	nature
_oy	boy, toy	u̠	pull, full
p	paper, tap	ur	urge, turn, fur
ph	phone, elephant, graph	ūr	cure, pure
qu_	quick, queen	v	voice, save
r	ram, born, ear	w_	will, wash
s	sun, ask, yes	wh_	white, what
_s̲	toes, hose	wr_	write
_s̲_	vision, confusion	_x	extra, ax
ss̠	fission	_x̲_	exist, example
sh	show, bishop, fish	y_	yes, yet
t	tall, sets, bit	_y	baby, happy (when it is the only vowel in a final unstressed syllable)
th	thick, three		
t̲h̲	this, feather, bathe		
_tch	itch, patch		
_ti̲_	nation, station, *also* question		
t̠u	congratulate	_y̆_	cymbal
u_, ŭ_	up, bus	_ȳ	cry, sky
ū̲	use, cute, *also* granulate	ẏ	zephyr, martyr
		z	zoo, nozzle, buzz

1. If a word ends in a silent *e*, as in **face**, the silent *e* is not marked. If a word ends in -*ed* pronounced **t**, as in **baked**, or **d**, as in **stayed**, no mark is needed. If the ending -*ed* forms a separate syllable pronounced ėd, as in **load′ėd**, the *e* has a dot.

2. If there are two or three vowels in the same syllable and only one is marked, as in **beaū′ty, frĭend, rōgue**, or **breāk**, all the other vowels in the syllable are silent.

3. The Open Court diacritical marks in the Pronunciation Key make it possible to indicate the pronunciation of most unfamiliar words without respelling.

ad·mire′ *v.* to be pleased with; to think well of

aisle (īl) *n.* the space between counters in a store or between seats in a theater, church, or bus

al·to·geth′er *adv.* entirely; completely

a·măz′ing *adj.* surprising; astonishing

am′ble *v.* to stroll; to walk at an easy pace

ān′cient *adj.* very old; in times long past

an·nounce′ *v.* to tell about something

ap·point′ *v.* to choose for a job

Ar′ab *n.* a person from one of several countries, such as Egypt or Saudi Arabia, east and south of the Mediterranean Sea

a·rē′na *n.* an area surrounded by seats and used for sports or entertainment

at·tract′ *v.* to draw or pull close

ba·boon′ *n.* a large monkey with a long, doglike face

badg′er *n.* a gray, furry animal that digs holes in the ground to live in

bank *n.* rising grounds at the edge of a stream or lake

ba·ton′ *n.* the stick used by the leader of a band or an orchestra for keeping time to the music and directing the players

beam *v.* to smile brightly in delight

be·lief′ *n.* what is thought to be true

be·wil′der *v.* to confuse; to puzzle

bis′cuit *n.* a small, hard cake given to dogs to keep their teeth healthy and satisfy their need to chew

bliz′zard *n.* a bad snowstorm with heavy snow, high winds, and a very low temperature

bob *v.* to move quickly up and down

bound *v.* to make long leaps; to jump

bow *v.* to bend low

breeze *n.* a soft, gentle wind

bril′liant *adj.* sparkling; very bright

bud *n.* a leaf or flower not fully open

burst *n.* a sudden, short action, as a *burst* of speed

calf (caf) *n.* a young cow

calm (cäm) *adj.* still and quiet; not moving

cam′o·mile *n.* a plant that has strong-smelling leaves and flowers used for medicine and tea

can′yon *n.* a deep, narrow valley

cha·me′le on *n.* a small lizard that can change the color of its skin

Cha·nuk·kah (hä′nuk·ka) *n.* an eight-day Jewish holiday in late November or in December, often called the Festival of Lights (*also spelled* **Hanukkah**)

char′ac·ter *n.* a person or animal in a story or play

chick′a·dee *n.* a small bird that is mostly gray and white but has a black throat and head

chil′ly *adj.* cool enough to be uncomfortable

chin rest *n.* the part on the body of a violin on which a player rests the chin while playing (*see also* **violin**)

claim *v.* 1. to say you own something 2. to say something is true

clam *n.* an animal that lives in water and has a soft body enclosed by two shells

clar·i·net′ *n.* a musical instrument shaped like a long tube with holes in it, played by blowing into a mouthpiece while closing and opening the holes with fingers

Pronunciation Key

VOWELS: sat, hăve, āble, fäther, all, câre, àlone; yet, brĕad, mē, loadèd; it, practĭce, pīlot, machīne; hot, nō, ôff, wagòn; foŏt, foōd; oil, toy; count, town; up, ūse, trŭth, pųll; mȳth, baby, crȳ, zephȳr.

CONSONANTS: cent, cider, cycle; chorus, chute; ġem; light, and though (silent), ghost; iñk, elephant; toes; them; special, meaşure, nation, nature.

clev′er *adj.* intelligent; smart; having a quick mind

cock *v.* to tip the head to one side and look questioningly at

com·pan′ion *n.* a friend

con′cen·trate *v.* to pay close attention to; to think hard about a single thing

con·fu′sion *n.* a mix-up caused when no one knows what is going on

con·sult′ *v.* to ask advice

con·tent′ *adj.* satisfied; pleased

con′ti·nent *n.* one of the seven large land masses on the earth: Africa, Antarctica, Asia, Australia, Europe, North America, and South America

con′tri·bu′tion *n.* help or money given; a gift

con·vinc′ing *n.* proof; a way of making something believable

cor′du·roy *n.* a strong, hard-wearing cloth with ridges

cour'ti·er *n.* a person who is part of a royal court; one who takes care of the needs of a king or queen

coy·o·te (kī ō'tē *or* kī'ōt) *n.* a small wolflike animal

cra'dle *v.* to lay or rock either in a cradle or as if in a cradle

crook *v.* to bend or curve

crop *n.* what is grown in a field or on a farm in a season

cru'el *adj.* hurtful; painful; unkind

cu'ri·os'i·ty *n.* the desire to know or find out something

cur'rant *adj.* made with currants (small, dried fruits that are like raisins)

cus'tom *n.* a habit; a rule

dart *v.* to move very quickly

dash *v.* to run very fast

def'i·nite·ly *adv.* certainly; surely

de·sire' *n.* a strong feeling of wanting something

de·spair' *v.* to lose hope

des'per·ate·ly *adv.* recklessly or wildly because of a bad situation

dis·cour'age *v.* to cause to lose hope

dis·like' *v.* to have no liking for; not to like very strongly

dis·please' *v.* to anger; to annoy

dose *n.* the amount of medicine taken at one time

dread'ful *adj.* frightening; terrible

drei'del (drād'əl) *n.* a four-sided top having Hebrew letters on it that is spun in a game played during Chanukkah

ech'o *v.* to repeat; to bounce off and return

el'e·va·tor *n.* a cage or platform used to move people or things up and down, usually from one floor to another in buildings

em'er·ald *n.* a valuable bright-green stone used in making jewelry

en·chant'ed *adj.* magical

en·cour'age *v.* to give courage or hope to; to help or cheer on

e·nor'mous *adj.* very large; huge

es'ca·la·tor *n.* a moving stairway

e·vent' *n.* an important happening

ex·claim' *v.* to cry out suddenly

ex·ert' *v.* to try very hard; to use one's strength

ex·per'i·ment *n.* a test to find out or prove something

ex'pert *n.* a person who is very good at doing or knows a great deal about a particular thing

ex·tinct' *adj.* not living now; no longer alive or existing

fā′ble *n.* 1. a story that teaches a lesson or moral 2. a story that is not true; a lie

fact *n.* something that is true or real

fail *v.* to miss; not to succeed; to disappoint

fair *adj.* pretty

fär′a·way′ *adj.* distant; a long way off

fas·ten (fas′sen) *v.* to tie; to join together

fā′vor·īte *n.* a person or thing that is liked best

feast *n.* a big meal with a great deal of food

fetch *v.* to go for and bring back; to get

fierce *adj.* wild and powerful; dangerous

fin′ger·board′ *n.* a piece of wood that lies under the strings of a violin or similar instrument (The player's fingers press the strings against the board to make different sounds. *See also* **violin.**)

fit *adj.* right for a job; proper; suitable

flap *n.* a piece of cloth used as a door to a tent

flat′ter·er *n.* a person who praises or says something good without meaning it

flax *n.* the part of a certain plant from which thread can be made

flint *n.* a hard stone that makes sparks when struck against steel

flut′ter *v.* to flap in the air (as wings)

fōre′foŏt *n.* one of the front feet of an animal

fōre′leg *n.* one of the front legs of an animal

fôrt′night *n.* two weeks; fourteen days and nights

fos′sil *n.* the remains of plants or animals that died a long time ago

fun′nel *n.* a large cone, with a tube at the bottom, used for filling bottles with small openings

fū′ry *n.* a rage; anger

gale *n.* a very high, strong wind

gruff *adj.* rough or rude; hoarse; harsh

gulp *v.* to swallow quickly and greedily

här′bȯr *n.* a part of a body of water (such as a sea or lake) that is protected and safe for ships and boats

haunch *n.* the upper part of a back leg of an animal; the hip and large part of the back leg

heärth *n.* the floor of a fireplace

hedge *n.* a fence of growing bushes or low trees

high′-pitched′ *adj.* having a sharp tone

his′tȯ·ry *n.* 1. a record of events that happened in the past 2. events that happened in the past

hōe *v.* to use a garden tool for weeding

hōld *v.* to contain

hon·ors (on′ors) *n. pl.* titles or rewards given for great public service

hū′mȯr *n.* fun; something that is amusing

hur′ri·cane *n.* a bad storm with strong winds and usually with heavy rain (Hurricanes begin over water and often move toward land, where they may cause much damage.)

ice′berg *n.* a very large, floating piece of ice found in oceans

im·plore′ *v.* to beg

im·press′ *v.* to have a strong effect, often on the feelings of others

in·dè·pend′ènt *adj.* free; thinking and acting for oneself

in·quīr′y *or* **in′quir·y** *n.* a question; a seeking for information

in′sect *n.* a small animal (such as a grasshopper or fly) with six legs and often two pairs of wings

in·vis′i·ble *adj.* not possible to see

Jè·rū′sà·lèm *n.* an ancient, holy city in Israel; the capital of Israel

King Sol′ȯ·mȯn *n.* an ancient, Jewish king who was very wise and peaceful

king′dȯm *n.* all of the people and land that a king and queen rule over

lane *n.* a narrow road

ledge *n.* a shelf

lōōm *n.* a machine for weaving thread into cloth

lōōn *n.* a large diving bird that eats fish and is known for its loud, wild cries

lūke′warm *adj.* just a little warm; not cold or hot

lurk *v.* to lie in wait; to hide

lust′y *adj.* full of energy; loud

204

lūte *n.* a pear-shaped musical instrument, having strings like a guitar, that people have played for thousands of years

mag'nėt *n.* a piece of stone or metal that pulls iron to it

mag·nif'i·cėnt *adj.* splendid; very large or richly decorated; grand

Mä'mä·cï'tä *n.* a form of the Spanish word *mama*, for mother

Man'dȧ·rin *adj.* Chinese; (Mandarin tea is a certain kind of Chinese tea.)

mar'i·gōld *n.* a plant that has yellow or gold-colored flowers

mar'rōw *n.* a soft material found inside most bones

mass *n.* a large number, size, or amount

mĕad'ōw *n.* an open field of grass

meal'wȯrm *n.* a wormlike stage in a beetle's life, during which small animals such as some birds and reptiles often feed on the insect

mel'ȯ·dy *n.* a tune

milk'maid *n.* a girl or woman who milks cows

mill *n.* a place where wheat or other grain is ground into flour

mil'lėt *n.* a kind of grass seed used for food

Pronunciation Key

VOWELS: sat, hăve, āble, fäther, ạll, câre, ȧlone; yet, brĕad, mē, loadėd; it, practĭce, pīlot, machïne; hot, nō, ôff, wagȯn; fŏŏt, fōōd; oil, toy; count, town; up, ūse, trŭth, pụll; mȳth, baby, crȳ, zephȳr.

CONSONANTS: cent, cider, cycle; c̅horus, c̲hute; ġem; light, and though (silent), ghost; iñk, elephant; toeṣ; t̲hem; speçial, meaṣure, natịon, natụre.

mĭn'er·ȧl *n.* anything that comes from the earth that is not animal or plant

min'is·ter *n.* a person who helps a king or other government leader

mĭr'ȧ·cle *n.* a wonderful or amazing event that no one expected would happen

mĭr'rȯr *v.* to reflect as if in a mirror

mis'chĭef *n.* a childish action that often causes harm or trouble

moan *v.* to make a low sound in pain or sorrow

mol'ė·cūle *n.* the smallest possible part of any substance; the smallest part into which any substance can be divided and still be the same substance; molecules cannot be seen

mul'bĕr·ry *n.* a tree that has purple or white berries

mū·ṣi'cịȧn *n.* a person who sings, writes music, or plays a musical instrument

night′in·gale *n.* a small bird that sings beautifully, usually at night

nō′tĭce *n.* an announcement placed where many people can read it

Oĕd′i·pus *n.* a traveler, in Greek myths, who solved the riddle of the Sphinx and became king of Thebes

ō′pȧl *n.* a stone (often used in jewelry) that seems to change colors when it is moved in the light

or′chĕs·trȧ *n.* a group of musicians who play instruments in concerts

out′stretched′ *adj.* stretched out; reaching out for

ō′ver·ạlls *n. pl.* pants having a top part that covers the chest and straps that go over the shoulders

ō·ver·hear′ *v.* to hear something one is not supposed to hear; to hear by accident

ō·ver·joyed′ *adj.* very happy

ō′ver·sized *adj.* larger than usual

ō·ver·turn′ *v.* to upset; to turn upside down

pad *v.* to walk softly

pȧ·gō′dȧ *adj.* layered like a tower *n.* a tower having many stories that is often found in Japan, India, or China

pale *adj.* light colored

pant *v.* to breathe hard and rapidly

pärt *v.* to open up; to separate

pär′ti·cle *n.* something very small, such as a molecule

peer *v.* to peek out at something

per·mit′ *v.* to let; to allow

pė·tū′nï·ȧ *n.* a plant that has pink, red, white, or purple flowers shaped like trumpets

phĕas′ȧnt *n.* a bird with a long tail (The male pheasant has brightly colored feathers.)

pïerce *v.* to make a hole in; to go through

plow *v.* to turn over and break up the soil to get it ready for planting

pluck *v.* to tug or give a pull such as on guitar strings

pȯ·si′tiȯn *n.* the way a person or thing stands, is held, or is placed

pōst *v.* to put up a poster or notice

pound *n.* a place where stray animals are kept

pres′ent·ly *adv.* soon; before long

prė·serve′ *v.* to keep in the same way or condition

proud′ly *adv.* in a way that shows a person is thinking too highly of oneself

quar′rėl *n.* an argument; an angry fight with words

ras′cal *n.* a person who is not honest

reg′u·lar *adj.* usual; ordinary

re·hearse′ *v.* to practice in order to prepare for a performance

re·märk′a·ble *adj.* unusual; uncommon; worth noticing

re·place′ *v.* to put one thing in place of another; to substitute

rep·re·sent′ *v.* to act for; to stand for something else

ri·dic′u·lous *adj.* silly; foolish

ru′by *n.* a valuable red stone used in jewelry

ruf′fle *v.* to disturb the smoothness of anything

rum′ble *v.* to growl; to make a noise like thunder

rush *v.* to move very fast

sand′bank *n.* a large pile of sand

sap·phire (sa′phire) *n.* a valuable blue stone used in jewelry

scal′lop *n.* an animal, with a body enclosed in two shells, that lives in water

scamp′er *v.* to move or run quickly

scoot *v.* to move quickly

scrap *n.* a small piece

scut′ter *v.* to run off in fright; to scurry

seek *v.* to look for

Pronunciation Key

VOWELS: sat, hăve, āble, fäther, all, câre, alone; yet, brĕad, mē, loadĕd; it, practĭce, pīlot, machīne; hot, nō, ôff, wagon; fŏŏt, fōōd; oil, toy; count, town; up, ūse, trŭth, pull; mўth, baby, crȳ, zephўr.

CONSONANTS: cent, cider, cycle; chorus, chute; ġem; light, and though (silent), ghost; ink, elephant; toes; them; special, measure, nation, nature.

sep′a·rāte′ed *v.* to divide or to keep apart

shrug *v.* to raise and lower the shoulders to show that you do not know or care

sï *adv.* a Spanish word that means yes

sick·le *n.* a farm tool with a sharp, curved edge and a short handle; used to cut grass and wheat

sïeve *n.* a sifter; a tool with a screen, that is used to drain water from foods or to separate small pieces from bigger pieces

sink *v.* to go down; to become lower than before

site *n.* the place where something happens; the land on which a building or town stands

siz′zling *adj.* making a hissing noise, usually because of heat

slave *n.* a person owned by another person

slȳ *adj.* sneaky; tricky

soc′cer *n.* a game in which one team tries to get a round ball through the goal of the other team by moving the ball with any parts of the body except arms and hands

sō′lō *adj.* lone; without any others

sōw *v.* to plant seeds

spâre *v.* to save someone the pain or work of

spin′dle *n.* a pin on a spinning wheel used to twist or wind thread

spin′ning wheel *n.* a machine, with a large wheel and a spindle, that is used for making thread

spit′ting *adj.* making a sizzling or hissing sound

splen′did *adj.* very fine or fancy; magnificent; grand

splen′dȯr *n.* beauty or brilliance; magnificence

stalk (stạk) *n.* the stem of a plant

stocks *n.* a wooden frame with holes for arms or legs in which people had to sit for long periods of time as punishment

stray *n.* a lost animal

stụ̄′dĭ·ō *n.* the room in which an artist works

suf′fer *v.* to have pain

sur·round′ *v.* to circle; to be on all sides of; to enclose

swish *v.* to move with a hissing or light brushing sound

sўc′à·more *n.* a tree with bark that flakes off; a buttonwood tree

ten′der *adj.* soft; easily cut or chewed

tĕr′ri·fied *adj.* to be frightened very badly; to be afraid

tĕr′rȯr *n.* great fear or dread

tĕr′rȯr-strick′ėn *adj.* overcome with great fear

Thebes *n.* a city in ancient Greece

thorn *n.* a part of a plant that is pointed and sharp enough to break the skin

thresh *v.* to separate grain (such as wheat) from the stalk

tī′dy *v.* to make something neat; to straighten

top′ple *v.* to fall; to tumble down

tor·nā′dō *n.* a bad windstorm with strong, twisting winds (*also called* **twister**)

trem′bling *adv.* shaking; shivering

trom′bone *or* **trom·bone′** *n.* a musical instrument, in the horn family, with a mouthpiece at one end, a bell-shaped opening at the other end, and two long tubes in between; one tube slides to change the pitch of the sound

trum′pėt *n.* a musical instrument, in the horn family, with a mouthpiece at one end, a bell-shaped opening at the other end, and three valves that are pushed down to change the sound

truñk *n.* 1. an elephant's long nose 2. a large chest for holding clothes for traveling

tūne *v.* 1. to get musical instruments ready for playing by setting to the correct pitch 2. *n.* a musical melody

tur′nip *n.* a plant with a large, round, yellow or white root that is eaten as a vegetable

twang *v.* to make a sharp, trembling sound such as a guitar makes

twist′ing *adj.* winding; turning around and around

twitch *v.* to jerk; to pull quickly

un·com·fort·a·ble (un·cȯmf′tȧ·ble *or* un·cȯm′fȯr·tȧ·ble) *adj.* not comfortable; not pleasant 2. uneasy

un·com′mȯn *adj.* not common; unusual; rare

un·fit′ *adj.* not fit; not right for a job

un·for′tů·nȧte·ly *adv.* in a way that seems unlucky

un·ū′şū·ȧl *adj.* not usual; not common; rare

up′right *adj.* standing straight up

up·set′ *v.* to turn over

vet·er·i·nâr′ï·ȧn *n.* a doctor who treats animals

vil′lȧġe *n.* a group of homes and businesses, usually in the country; a community, usually smaller than a town

vī·ȯ·lin′ *n.* a musical instrument that is usually played by moving a bow across its strings; a fiddle

wail *v.* to cry loudly, usually in pain or grief

wätch′mȧn *n.* a person who guards a place

wạ′ter·cȯl′ȯr *n.* 1. a paint that mixes with water 2. a painting made with watercolors

weave *v.* to make cloth by putting threads over and under each other, as on a loom

weav′er *n.* a person who makes cloth by weaving

weep *v.* to cry

wept *v.* cried (*see* **weep**)

wheel′bar′rōw *n.* a light, one-wheeled cart used for moving heavy loads

whim′per *v.* to cry with weak, broken sounds

whine *v.* to cry or howl for a long time

wīnd′ing *adj.* twisting; bending; curving

yañk *v.* to pull with a jerking motion

Yid′dish *n.* a language spoken by some Jewish people

yip *v.* to bark sharply